Real Solutions
Weight Loss Workbook

SECOND EDITION

Toni Piechota, MS, MPH, RDN

eat right® Academy of Nutrition and Dietetics

Cathy Iammartino, *Publisher*
Christina Sanders, *Acquisitions and Development Manager*
Brooke Pudar, *Development Editor*
Elizabeth Nishiura, *Manager of Production and Digital Content Development*

Real Solutions Weight Loss Workbook, Second Edition
ISBN 978-0-88091-486-4

The views expressed in this publication are those of the authors and do not necessarily reflect policies and/or official positions of the Academy of Nutrition and Dietetics. Mention of product names in this publication does not constitute endorsement by the authors or the Academy of Nutrition and Dietetics. The Academy of Nutrition and Dietetics disclaims responsibility for the application of the information contained herein.

10 9 8 7 6 5 4 3 2 1

For more information on the Academy of Nutrition and Dietetics, visit: www.eatright.org.

Contents

Preface

Real Solutions Weight Loss Workbook provides practical guidance for people seeking to lose weight and maintain weight loss, and for health professionals working in the weight loss field.

This engaging workbook incorporates the principles of behavior modification: self-monitoring, mindful eating, realistic goal setting, and creating a supportive environment. Negative self-talk and low self-confidence can interfere with effective weight control. Therefore, *Real Solutions* guides the reader to challenge these negative thoughts through self-reflective exercises. The workbook also presents basic facts about weight loss as well as guidelines for safe and effective physical activity in an easy-to-understand format.

Real Solutions Weight Loss Workbook is a comprehensive tool that both informs the reader and encourages thoughtful action.

Introduction

Linda's alarm jolts her awake at 6:00 A.M. She rolls out of bed, still tired. Before she can pour a cup of coffee, her youngest son, Jason, runs up to her, crying about a bad dream. She picks him up to comfort him when her teenager, Mike, rushes in, panicking about the course slip he forgot to have Linda sign. She heads to the kitchen, where the dog has dumped his water all over the floor. She scribbles her signature on Mike's form, cleans up after the dog, pours a bowl of cereal for Jason, and finally makes it to the coffee pot. Linda has barely enough time to shower and run a comb through her hair before squeezing into a pair of pants that she realizes no longer fit. Discouraged, she slips on a dress instead and runs out the door without breakfast. After dropping the kids at school, she gets to work. One more cup of coffee with vanilla creamer and Linda gets right to her to-do list. She doesn't look up until noon.

By now, Linda is famished. She breaks away to the closest fast-food place for a quick lunch and, mindful of her "pants fiasco" that morning, orders what seems like a low-calorie meal (but in reality supplies half her calorie needs for the entire day): a chicken wrap, baked chips instead of fries, and a large nonfat frappe to keep her awake through the afternoon. She eats at her desk while answering e-mails.

Linda hits the vending machine for a quick snack around 3 P.M. When she wraps up her work day at 5 P.M., she drives her kids from school to their after-school activities. On the way home, they hit the drive-through and scarf down burgers and fries. Back at home, Linda gets Jason to bed and helps Mike with homework. At 11 P.M., she finally has some time alone. She breaks out the ice cream and enjoys the only peaceful moment of her day. She gets to bed at midnight, only to start again at 6 A.M. the next day.

Does Linda's day sound familiar? Based on a national survey from 2010, two out of every three American adults are overweight or obese. That number has more than doubled since the 1970s! It's no wonder. Changes in the American way of life over the past several decades have fostered this trend. Time crunches, fast food, sedentary jobs, misinformation about nutrition, sleep deprivation, and stressful lives are all culprits in today's obesity epidemic.

Store shelves are overflowing with high-fat, low-fiber convenience foods that can pack on pounds. High-calorie fast foods are often cheaper and more easily available than fresh fruits and vegetables. Portion sizes have increased—even tripling in some cases—while our dependence on technology and cars encourages inactivity. Busy lives make healthy eating an afterthought, and a lack of social support makes room for food as a source of comfort. A stressful day at work prompts a trip to the vending machine. An argument with a family member is forgotten with a bag of cookies.

To make things worse, popular books and weight loss products cash in on the trend by selling "quick fixes" that claim to yield fast results with little effort. What usually happens? Most people don't lose much weight. If they do, they often gain it back—and then some—and are left feeling discouraged.

When everything around you seems to encourage weight gain, how do you fight back?

If you decide you're ready to make a change, you first need to arm yourself with accurate information. But knowledge does not equal behavior. Changing takes a lot of time and energy, and, despite all of the competing demands of life, weight loss must be a priority. You may need to reflect on some of the reasons you eat, such as for emotional comfort, or because of social pressure. By considering the role of food in your life, you will position yourself to find effective solutions for lifelong change.

This workbook will walk you through the most current weight loss recommendations. The exercises in each chapter will help you identify areas of concern and define strategies to address your needs and achieve your goals. Whether you need the knowledge to make effective changes, guidance to explore your issues, or ideas to keep weight off, you will find what you need in the chapters that follow.

"Know Thyself"

Losing weight and maintaining that weight loss may be the biggest challenges you have ever faced. Before jumping in, it helps to do a little self-assessment and explore your reasons for wanting (or not wanting) to change. Since your physical and emotional health may be among your reasons to make a change, looking at how your weight affects your well-being is a good place to start.

What's Your Risk?

Excess weight can affect your quality of life in many ways: socially, financially, and personally. (See **Hazards of Obesity**, below.) Some research suggests that excess weight may be associated with bias in the workplace, low self-esteem, and negative interactions in relationships. Excess weight leads some people to avoid certain activities, such as going to the beach or flying on a plane. Being overweight or obese also puts you at risk for many health issues. Risk for diabetes, high blood pressure, and certain other diseases increases as weight increases, and the higher your weight, the greater your risk.

Hazards of Obesity

People who are overweight or obese have an increased risk of the following hazards:

- Coronary artery disease
- Stroke
- Diabetes mellitus
- High blood pressure
- Sleep apnea

- Osteoarthritis and bone and joint pain
- Musculoskeletal injuries
- Acid reflux
- Lung and breathing problems
- Complications during surgery

- Reproductive challenges
- Fatigue
- Low self-esteem
- Social stigmatization
- Physical inability to take part in some activities

Determine Your Body Mass Index (BMI)

Body weight alone is not an accurate indicator of health risk. Excess body fat is. How do you know if you have excess body fat? Excess body fat is usually estimated by a weight-height assessment called body mass index (BMI). While BMI does not directly measure body fat, a high BMI can be an indicator of excess fat.

To find your BMI, use the National Heart, Lung and Blood Institute's BMI calculator (www.nhlbi.nih.gov/health/educational/lose_wt/BMI/bmicalc.htm) or use this formula:

$$\text{Weight} \times 703 \div \text{Height} \div \text{Height} = \text{BMI}$$

1. Multiply your weight (in pounds) by 703: _____

2. Divide that number by your height (in inches): _____

3. Divide that new number by your height (in inches) again: _____

This final number is your BMI.

For example, let's find the BMI of someone who weighs 210 pounds and is 62 inches tall.

$$BMI = 210 \times 703 \div 62 \div 62 = 38.4.$$

Now that you know your BMI, use the Evaluating Your Body Mass Index chart (below) to help interpret it. For adults, a BMI of 25 to 29.9 suggests that you are overweight, and a BMI of 30 or more suggests that you are obese. Although BMI can help identify health risk, not everyone should strive for a "normal weight" BMI. Your doctor or registered dietitian nutritionist (RDN) can help you decide what number is right for you.

Evaluate Your Body Mass Index (BMI)

Weight Classification	BMI
Underweight	Below 18.5
Normal weight	18.5–24.9
Overweight	25.0–29.9
Obese	30.0 and above

Source: National Heart, Lung, and Blood Institute, National Institutes of Health. Aim for a Healthy Weight: Calculate Your Body Mass Index. www.nhlbi.nih.gov/health/educational/lose_wt/BMI/bmicalc.htm.

Determine Your Waist Circumference

Another indicator of health risk is the location of fat on your body. Even if your weight is in the "normal" range, fat that accumulates around the waist and abdomen tends to pose more health risks than fat in the hips and thighs. According to the National Institutes of Health (NIH), risks of heart disease and diabetes increase in men whose waist circumferences are greater than 40 inches. For women, these risks increase when their waist circumference is greater than 35 inches.

To measure your waist circumference:

- Stand up straight, and wrap a tape measure around your bare abdomen above your hip bones.
- Keep the tape measure parallel to the floor.
- Breathe normally and pull the tape so it is snug but not digging into your waist.
- Record the number: _____ inches.

Reflecting on Your Personal Numbers

Depending on where you're starting from, the benchmarks for BMI and waist circumference described in this chapter may feel out of reach. Just remember that the main goal is to feel healthy and enjoy life at a weight that you can maintain. Losing small amounts of weight—even 5% of your total body weight—is a great accomplishment that can result in big improvements in your health.

Take a look at the numbers you recorded for your BMI and waist circumference. What is your reaction to these numbers? Write your thoughts or feelings below.

_____

_____

_____

Think back on the ways that excess weight can affect your well-being. What surprised you about this information? What didn't? Why?

_____

_____

_____

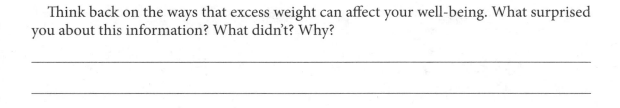

"I Do ...": Committing to a Healthy Weight

2

The process of achieving a healthy weight is kind of like marriage—both require a serious commitment, and you will undoubtedly run into obstacles. To ensure success over the long term, you will need to hold fast to your commitment and be prepared to deal with the challenges you will face.

The Stages of Commitment

Committing to weight loss is rarely a snap decision. You will probably go through a series of stages before you are ready to commit to a major decision like losing weight.

For most people, even deciding that there is a problem involves time and contemplation. At first, you may feel unsettled, wondering if something is wrong. _"Did I not get enough sleep? Do I need more coffee? Is this dissatisfaction something to worry about, or will it just blow over?"_

Once you've decided that there is indeed a problem, you might think, _"Maybe I am ready to make a change."_ You may consider taking action, but you may also wonder if you even _can_ change the situation.

Or, maybe you know the steps to take, but you are not sure that you are ready to take them. You may tell yourself, _"Maybe the problem is not that bad."_ Some people spend a lot of time wrestling with these first stages.

A specific moment may be the turning point that jars you into action. For example, a blood test that revealed a high blood sugar (glucose) level spurred one man to act. A woman, overwhelmed with embarrassment when a chair broke underneath her, suddenly realized that she was not just "pleasingly plump," as she had been telling herself.

For other people, small realizations gradually add up and lead to action. You may feel unhappy because you have to shop at special stores to find clothes that fit. Or you finally acknowledge, after so many summers, that the excess weight won't magically come off just because cantaloupe and peaches are in season. Eventually you decide, *"It's time to commit to making a change."*

What Am I Gaining? What Am I Losing?

The following exercises will help you explore your readiness to take on the weight loss challenge. To begin, consider the reasons you want to lose weight. Avoiding the hazards listed in Chapter 1: "Know Thyself" is a good way to start. Your reasons may also stem from emotional and social reasons or other aspects of your life.

Consider the ways that your weight affects you as well as those around you. What emotional response do you have while shopping for clothes, or when someone comments on your weight? Have your children adopted your eating habits? Do you spend less time with your partner? How would these things change if you lost weight?

Here are some examples to get you started:

- "I want to be able to go on bike rides with my children."
- "I want to be able to buy fashionable clothes."
- "I want to feel confident when I walk into a room."

Writing down why you want to lose weight can be a powerful motivator. List your reasons below. You may find it useful to keep this list in a visible place and to refer to it daily, especially when your spirits are sagging.

_____

_____

_____

_____

Of course, simply wanting to lose weight is not enough. Think about your current lifestyle. List some behaviors you will need to change if you are to lose weight. For example, "I will not be able to eat butter pecan ice cream every night," or "I will have to set aside some time for physical activity."

_____

_____

_____

_____

Although extra body weight may cause physical and emotional pain, there can be (believe it or not) benefits to being overweight or obese. Here are real-life examples of reasons why some people did not want to lose weight:

- "I don't have to deal with men making passes at me."
- "I can eat whatever I want to and don't have to worry."
- "I can avoid arguments with my family about eating healthy foods."
- "If I get rejected, I can blame it on my weight and don't feel as threatened."
- "I can maintain the belief that all I have to do to improve my life is to lose weight, and I know that if I *really* wanted to, I could."
- "I get out of doing things. Since my knees hurt, people sometimes do things for me."

Can you think of any reasons why you might want to stay at your current weight? List them here.

_____

_____

_____

_____

Now think of ways that you could cope with the reasons you listed. For example, if you worry about family arguments, you could write, "I can learn to be more assertive and stand up to my family. Eventually they will accept the changes."

_____

_____

_____

_____

If you are still on the fence about committing to weight loss, ask yourself:

1. "In 5 years, what will my life look like if I don't do anything?"

_____

_____

_____

2. "In 5 years, what will my life look like if I make this change? Why is that important to me?"

_____

_____

_____

3 The Battle of the Bulge: Are Your Weapons Drawn?

Use the questions in this chapter's quiz to assess whether you are ready to commit to weight loss. Your answers will help you identify the weapons you need in your arsenal before you go to battle.

Readiness Quiz

		Yes	No
1.	Do you have a source of support to offer guidance and help you stay motivated to lose weight?	☐	☐
2.	Do you have time scheduled for physical activity?	☐	☐
3.	Have you thought about a realistic weight loss goal?	☐	☐
4.	Do you believe that losing weight will improve all other areas of your life?	☐	☐
5.	Do you think that you will have failed if you go off your weight management program from time to time?	☐	☐
6.	Are you willing to do some self-exploration?	☐	☐
7.	If it will help you, are you willing to seek outside aid, such as a counselor, support group, registered dietitian nutritionist (RDN), or personal trainer?	☐	☐
8.	Have you visualized what your life will be like when you reach your goal weight? (For example, what will you have for lunch? How will you fit physical activity into your daily routine?)	☐	☐
9.	Are you willing to invest the mental energy required to learn about calories and make daily decisions regarding your weight?	☐	☐
10.	Are you willing to keep records of your eating and physical activity until you have learned to manage your weight?	☐	☐
11.	Do you accept the fact that managing your weight is a lifelong behavior and that it affects your entire life?	☐	☐
12.	Are you prepared to make weight loss one of your top priorities and deal with adverse reactions from family and friends?	☐	☐

Interpretation

1. **Do you have a source of support to offer guidance and help you stay motivated to lose weight?** Finding support is an important step to take before you start a weight loss program. Research has shown that people who have a good source of support do better with both long-term and short-term weight loss programs. Ideally, the people you live with and are closest to will support you, but you can also find support in other places, such as support groups.

2. **Do you have time scheduled for physical activity?** Your answer to this question serves a couple purposes. First, it tells you whether you have thought about the practical considerations involved in weight loss, such as when you will fit in physical activity. Second, it tells you whether or not you recognize the critical role of physical activity in long-term weight management.

3. **Have you thought about a realistic weight loss goal?** Many people have a long history of disappointment when it comes to weight loss, and setting unrealistic goals is a contributing factor. For instance, if your lowest adult weight was 150 pounds at age 20, and you have weighed 200 pounds for 25 years, then a goal weight of 120 pounds is probably not realistic. Could you be happy at a higher goal weight?

   > ### Setting Realistic Goals
   >
   > Use these questions as a guide to consider what might be a realistic goal weight.
   > - What was my lowest adult weight?
   > - What weight have I been able to maintain in the past?
   > - How much physical activity am I willing and able to do?
   > - How much am I willing to change?

4. **Do you believe that losing weight will improve all other areas of your life?** Weight loss will improve your health, and may improve your self-image or your relationships. However, there is no guarantee that losing weight will drastically improve your life overall. Your spouse may find other things about you to criticize, or you may remain as shy as you always have been. Recognize that weight loss will probably improve your quality of life, but it will not fix everything.

5. **Do you think that you will have failed if you go off your weight management program from time to time?** Weight management is a lifelong process and must be viewed as such. If you expect to be perfect all the time, you are setting yourself up for failure down the road. A more helpful approach is to set realistic goals each day and accept that there will inevitably be days when you will not fully meet them.

6. **Are you willing to do some self-exploration?** Weight loss can result in unexpected consequences. Some people say excess weight provides a feeling of protection, which is lost when pounds are shed. Your relationships may also change when you lose weight. For example, your spouse may become jealous of your weight loss. After losing weight, one woman pressured her husband to lose weight as well, and she became angry when he refused. She felt that, since she had become more desirable to him, he should want to become more desirable to her. Be prepared to address such issues so they don't interrupt your progress.

7. **If it will help you, are you willing to seek outside aid, such as a counselor, support group, registered dietitian nutritionist (RDN), or personal trainer?** Some people find that they need to resolve other problems before they can be ready to lose weight. Karen, a wife, office manager, and mother of three, went

through counseling while she was in a weight loss program and learned to be more assertive and place her needs first. She has been able to maintain her weight loss for several years, in part because she was better prepared to deal with the emotional issues that can interfere with weight management.

8. **Have you visualized what your life will be like when you reach your goal weight?** Maintaining a lower body weight involves some changes. You may need to spend less time on other priorities and more time exercising. You will also need to make daily decisions about how your food choices fit within your calorie budget and perhaps cut back significantly on your favorite foods. For example, you may have to trade in your traditional Friday night banana split for a small frozen yogurt. Have you thought about these things? Are you ready for them?

9. **Are you willing to invest the mental energy required to learn about calories and make daily decisions regarding your weight?** You would not try to manage your financial budget without looking at prices. Likewise, you can't manage your calorie budget without looking at calories. You will have to put in time and effort to learn about portion sizes and the calorie content of the foods you eat so you can make the best choices and increase your likelihood of success. This process is time consuming at first, but it will become easier over time as you learn which foods fit into your plan.

10. **Are you willing to keep records of your eating and physical activity until you have learned to manage your weight?** To manage your finances, you keep and review records of how much money you deposit in the bank and how much you withdraw. The same principle applies in weight loss, except that you record your calories instead of dollars. For weight loss, your goal is to create a calorie deficit by consuming fewer calories than you use in physical activity. Keeping and reviewing daily records helps you decide whether foods fit within your "budget." This activity requires a lot of self-awareness and commitment. However, it is one of the most effective techniques for ensuring weight loss.

11. **Do you accept the fact that managing your weight is a lifelong behavior and that it affects your entire life?** People who have been successful in maintaining weight loss recognize that it is a lifelong process. The dietary choices necessary to lose weight are the same choices required to maintain that loss. Although the process does get easier, it does not end.

12. **Are you prepared to make weight loss one of your top priorities and deal with adverse reactions from family and friends?** One of the hardest parts of weight loss is that it often competes with other demands. (Women can be especially vulnerable because they tend to place the needs of others above their own.) Making weight loss a priority means that you have to exercise even if you're tired and would rather sleep. Sometimes, friends or family members will sabotage your efforts. They may take it personally when you no longer wish to partake in banana splits on Friday nights. They may not understand why you don't bake chocolate chip cookies anymore. Are you ready to tackle these challenges?

Setting the Stage

Let's take a look at some strategies that can enhance your success as you begin a weight loss program, including seeking social support, drawing from past successes and existing skills, and identifying possible roadblocks.

Who can you count on to support you in eating and activity goals? Consider friends, family members, coworkers, neighbors, or weight loss support groups.

_____

_____

_____

What are some areas of your life that are going well? What skills do you already have that you can apply to your weight loss plan? For example, if you have developed systems to make sure that your kids are always organized when they go to school, perhaps you can apply those same organizational skills to plan and prepare healthy meals.

_____

_____

_____

Consider your previous efforts to lose weight. First, think about the times you succeeded. What helped you be successful? For example, did you do better when you budgeted 150 calories for favorite foods each day? Or when you made meals in advance?

_____

_____

_____

When you have had trouble losing weight, what got in your way? Was it stress? A break from your routine? Boredom?

_____

_____

_____

Could these roadblocks become a problem again? Think about some ways to overcome them. Ask the people in your support network for ideas.

_____

_____

_____

Look at your schedule and other potential sources of stress in your life. What is going on in your life that will compete with weight management for your time and energy?

_____

_____

_____

Can you let go of some of the stress? For example, can you delegate responsibilities or postpone certain commitments?

_____

_____

_____

When you face roadblocks, look back at your answers to these questions and consider which of these strategies can help you get past the obstacles.

5 Principles of Weight Loss

Reasons for Obesity

There is firm evidence that genes play a role in body weight and in health risk. Looking at your parents and their health histories can give you some idea of your susceptibility to obesity, to a particular body shape, and to certain diseases, such as heart disease and diabetes. In addition, hormones and brain chemicals affect your appetite, telling your brain, "Eat!" or "Stop eating!"

But if the causes are genetic, hormonal, or chemical, why has obesity only recently become such a big problem? Many environmental factors currently work together to create what researchers call an *obesigenic environment* (that is, an environment conducive to excess weight gain). High-fat, high-sugar, low-fiber diets and inactive lifestyles are the norm. The multibillion-dollar food industry competes relentlessly for our money by bombarding us with food advertisements and bigger meal deals (meaning more fat and calories for your money). Billboards, magazines, television, online ads, and the radio constantly remind us of all the different delicious flavors waiting for consumption. You may not even be thinking about a char-grilled hamburger with sharp cheddar cheese, crisp bacon, creamy mayonnaise, and fresh lettuce and tomatoes on a lightly toasted bun. However, after you hear the burger being vividly described in a commercial, you cannot get it off your mind, and suddenly you're at the drive-through window. Food advertising, a daily threat to weight loss, is difficult to avoid.

Beyond advertising, the food industry contributes to the obesity epidemic by cashing in on our biology. Manufacturers create foods that are high in fat and sugar (and thus high in calories) because they taste so good and therefore sell very well.

In addition to environmental factors, psychological and social factors also influence weight. For example, loneliness is prevalent in the United States. Many overweight and obese people say that their best friend is food. Giving up the comfort that food brings is like letting go of your best friend. In our high-stress world, you can always count on food to be there for you. When you have a deadline, you may not feel you have time to go for a walk or take a hot bath. But you can eat chips while you work.

Many of these factors may affect your weight. Is there one specific factor that is most important for you? Complete the Eating Self-Assessment (Appendix 1) to help you target your biggest challenges.

Basics of Weight Loss: Calories In, Calories Out

Now that you have a sense of the factors that contribute to weight gain, let's turn our attention to the basics of weight loss, starting with calories. Here are the facts:

- A calorie is a unit of energy.
- Calories in food come from carbohydrates, proteins, fats, and alcohol.
- You take in calories by eating and drinking.
- You burn (use up) calories a few different ways:
  - By the work of living (breathing, digesting food, pumping blood, and so on),
  - Through activities of daily living (walking from the car to a building, making the bed, getting up to answer the phone, etc.), and
  - Through physical activity (biking, aerobics, jogging, and so on).
- Your body needs a certain amount of calories to function. It stores extra calories as fat.
- You gain body fat by taking in more calories than you burn.
- To lose body fat, you must create a calorie deficit by burning more calories than you take in.

Your weight, therefore, is a result of the balance between calories you take in and calories you burn. If you consume more calories than you burn, you gain weight. If you burn more calories than you consume, you lose weight.

You can control the number of calories you take in by selecting lower calorie foods and by eating less. In addition, you can increase the calories your body burns in everyday activities and physical activity. Keeping track of the number of calories you consume and burn, therefore, is an important part of weight loss.

Calories in Sample Foods

Food	Calories
1 chocolate kiss	25
1 fried chicken breast, extra crispy	375
1 quarter-pound fast-food cheeseburger	550
3-piece fried fish dinner	1,180
1 medium apple	100
1 fig bar	45
1 tablespoon butter	100
1 tablespoon sugar	50
6-ounce prime rib	600
6 ounces broiled shrimp	150

Check your understanding of the principles of weight loss with this quick activity. Use information from the charts on this page to answer the following questions:

1. How many minutes would you need to spend on an elliptical trainer to burn off the calories in a 6-ounce prime rib? _____

2. How many minutes would you need to spend on an elliptical trainer to burn off the calories in 6 ounces of broiled shrimp? _____

You can probably see by your answers that the amount of calories in the foods you choose has a big impact on how much work you need to do to lose weight. In the next section, you'll learn how to determine your daily calorie needs and how to make food choices that fit within your budget. You'll learn more about physical activity in Chapter 14: Move It and Lose It!

Calories Burned per Minute, by Individual's Weight*

Activity	140 Pounds	160 Pounds	180 Pounds	200 Pounds	220 Pounds
Housework (cleaning, washing dishes)	3.5	3.9	4.4	4.9	5.4
Dog walking	3.3	3.8	4.3	4.8	5.3
Brisk walking or circuit training	4.8	5.5	6.2	6.8	7.5
Power yoga	4.5	5.1	5.7	6.4	7.0
Stationary bike or elliptical trainer (exercising at a moderate intensity level)	5.6	6.4	7.2	8.0	8.8
Aerobic dance	6.6	7.5	8.5	9.4	10.3
Jogging (11-minute mile)	9.8	11.2	12.6	14.0	15.4
Bicycling (13 miles per hour)	10.5	11.9	13.3	14.7	16

*Values are approximate. Individual rates of calorie burning may vary.

How Many Calories Can You Eat and Still Lose Weight?

You have learned that to lose weight, you need to burn more calories than you consume. The number of calories you need to consume each day depends on your current weight, height, age, activity level, gender, and muscle mass. (Other factors, such as certain medications, may also affect weight. Talk to your doctor or RDN.)

You can find a calorie level appropriate for weight loss by multiplying the weight considered "ideal" for your height by 10 or 12. To find the "ideal" weight, use the following calculation:

1. Men: 106 pounds for the first 5 feet of height plus 6 pounds for every inch above 5 feet.

2. Women: 100 pounds for the first 5 feet of height plus 5 pounds for every inch above 5 feet.

The daily target generally ranges between 1,200 and 1,500 calories for women and 1,500 and 1,800 calories for men.

My daily calorie target: _____

This calculation can give you a starting place for your weight loss program without setting calorie levels that are too low to be healthy and achievable. Your doctor or RDN can also help you determine a healthy calorie level that fits your personal needs and goals.

Where Do Calories Come From?

Now that you know what your daily calorie target is, the next step is to plan how you will hit that target. To do this, it helps to understand why different foods have different numbers of calories. Let's start by taking a look at the two meal choices in the chart below.

Notice that Meal 2 is, by far, the lower-calorie choice. The main reason for this is that 10 ounces of prime rib contains many more calories than 6 ounces of tilapia. So why does prime rib have so many more calories than broiled tilapia? To understand, you must learn a little bit about where the calories in foods come from.

Calories (which are units of energy) in food come from four different sources: carbohydrate, protein, fat, and alcohol. Each of these energy sources makes a different calorie contribution to your diet:

- Carbohydrate provides 4 calories per gram.
- Protein provides 4 calories per gram.
- Fat provides 9 calories per gram.
- Alcohol provides 7 calories per gram.

Notice that gram for gram fat has more than double the calories of protein or carbohydrate. Because prime rib is high in fat

Calorie Comparison for Two Meals	
Meal 1	**Meal 2**
10-ounce prime rib	6-ounce broiled tilapia filet
Garden salad with 2 tablespoons of ranch dressing	Garden salad with 2 tablespoons of fat-free dressing
	1 cup steamed broccoli
	6-ounce baked potato
	1-ounce dinner roll
	½ cup fat-free frozen yogurt
1,075 calories	**580 calories**

(about 8 grams of fat per ounce of cooked beef), it is also high in calories. In contrast, tilapia is low in fat (about 1 gram of fat per ounce of cooked fish) and therefore much lower in calories.

All Calories Are Created Equal—Or Are They?

If your target for the day is 1,500 calories, does it matter which foods those calories come from? Yes and no.

You learned earlier that your body stores excess calories as body fat. This is true for all calories. A calorie is a calorie—it does not matter whether the source is carbohydrate, protein, fat, or alcohol. However, there are other factors to consider beyond the total number of calories consumed. Certain sources of calories may affect your appetite and hunger differently. The various sources of calories also affect blood sugar (glucose) differently, and they definitely vary in how they affect health.

Carbohydrates

Your body needs carbohydrates (also called "carbs") to fuel bodily functions and physical activity. Starch, sugars, and fiber are types of carbohydrates.

Whole grains, vegetables, fruits, and legumes (beans, peas, and lentils) are among the healthiest sources of carbohydrates. They are packed with vitamins, minerals, and fiber. Foods high in fiber provide a feeling of fullness, which can help when you're limiting calories. These foods also take longer for your body to digest and therefore provide a slow and steady source of energy. Fat-free and low-fat dairy foods are also healthy sources of carbohydrates, but they don't contain fiber.

Highly processed or refined sources of carbohydrates, such as corn syrup or white flour, aren't as healthy. These ingredients have little or no fiber and are stripped of much of their nutritional value during processing. Your body digests these carbs, which are found in foods like white bread and pastries and in soft drinks, more quickly than the complex carbs in whole grains, legumes, vegetables, and fruits.

Protein

Your body uses protein to build skin and muscle, among other things. Some research indicates that including protein in meals can reduce hunger and appetite. The healthiest choices include plant-based protein foods, such as beans and other legumes, which are naturally low in fat and high in fiber, and lean animal proteins, such as fish, skinless poultry, lean beef, lean pork, eggs, and fat-free or low-fat dairy products.

Fat

Because fat has 9 calories per gram, limiting all types of fatty foods will help you cut back on calories. Some types of dietary fats contain important nutrients and are part of a healthy diet. Other types increase your risk of heart disease and other health problems and should be limited or avoided.

- **Unsaturated fats**, which help with brain and heart health, are found in nuts, seeds, and vegetable oils (such as olive or canola oil). Most of the fat you consume should be unsaturated.
- **Saturated fats** are found in fatty meats, the skin of poultry, and reduced-fat or full-fat dairy products (such as 2% or whole milk, cream, and cheese). You should limit saturated fats.
- *Trans* **fats** negatively affect your blood cholesterol levels and raise the risk of heart disease. They are usually found in processed foods, such as many commercially baked products and snack foods, stick margarine, and shortening. All foods that list the word "hydrogenated" on the ingredients list have *trans* fats. Aim to avoid *trans* fats completely.

Alcohol

Alcoholic beverages do not provide vitamins, minerals, fiber, or other nutritional value. At 7 calories per gram, alcohol can make a dent in your calorie budget.

- 1½ ounces of hard alcohol contains about 100 calories.
- One 5-ounce glass of wine contains about 120 calories.
- One 12-ounce beer contains about 150 calories.

Women should limit their consumption to one drink or less per day. The limit for men is two drinks or less per day.

Nutrition and Weight Loss 6

In the previous chapters, you learned that staying within your daily calorie budget—how many calories you should consume each day—is an important element of weight loss. You have also learned where calories come from. Now, let's put these concepts together. In the coming chapters, you will learn how to make nutritious food choices that will keep you healthy, satisfied, and within your daily calorie budget. We'll begin by taking a look at choosing what to eat.

A Balanced Diet

Have you ever tried the diet-soda-and-sugarless-gum diet? You can always spot people on that kind of extreme diet—they are the ones who are obsessing about food, have the big bags under their eyes, and don't have the energy to tear open a packet of artificial sweetener. They neither look nor feel better, even if their clothes are looser. Weight loss is not just about being thinner. It's also about feeling better, inside and out.

Losing weight doesn't mean going to extremes. Skimping on nutrition can slow down your weight loss, make you lose muscle, and lead you to quit trying because you just don't feel well. The best way to lose weight and keep it off is to eat a balanced diet.

Using MyPlate Guidelines

One tool you can use to make sure you're eating a balanced diet is the MyPlate guide. This simple graphic shows you how to fill your plate with healthy choices that will support weight loss.

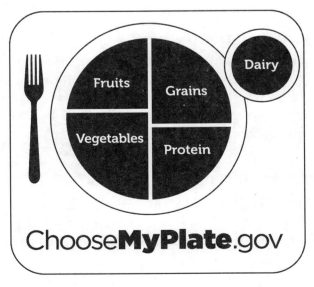

At the MyPlate website (www.choosemyplate.gov), you will find an abundance of free information about food choices, serving sizes, and meal patterns. Here are some guidelines from that site to get you started:

- **Fill half your plate with fruits and vegetables.** Vary your choices from meal to meal and day to day to get a wide range of vitamins and nutrients.
- **Focus on whole grains.** Whole grains (such as oatmeal, brown rice, 100% whole grain bread, and whole wheat pasta), are high in fiber and other nutrients. At least half of the servings of grains you eat each day should be whole grains. When choosing packaged foods, select those that list the words "whole grain" or "whole wheat" as the first ingredient on the ingredients list.
- **Choose lean proteins.** When you eat meat, choose lean cuts; also trim off any excess fat from meat and remove poultry skin before cooking. Eggs, fish, and seafood are other healthy, lean protein foods (prepare them without added oils or fats). Beans, lentils, and peas, which are plant-based proteins, are also good choices; they are low in fat and high in fiber.
- **Choose fat-free or low-fat dairy products.** Whole milk, reduced-fat (2%) milk, and many cheeses are high in saturated fat. Choosing low-fat or fat-free dairy products (such as skim or 1% milk or low-fat yogurt) is better for your heart and your waistline.
- **Limit foods that are high in fat.** You have already learned that gram for gram, fat is highest in calories. One tablespoon of butter, regular margarine, or oil has more than 110 calories. Other high-fat, high-calorie foods include mayonnaise, regular salad dressing, and avocado. When cooking, try low-fat or no-fat methods, such as broiling, grilling, roasting, or boiling, instead of frying foods.

Calorie-Free Foods

Many products made with artificial sweeteners, such as diet soda or sugar-free gelatin, have zero calories. Condiments such as mustard, vinegar, hot sauce, and lemon juice are so low in calories that you can use them in unlimited amounts to add flavor to your meals. (See Chapter 9: Examining Food Labels for information on how to find out the calories per serving in a food.)

What About Meal Replacements?

Meal replacements are foods that are packaged in calorie–controlled portions, such as reduced-calorie frozen meals or liquid supplements. Research has shown that these products can help with weight loss. You may want to follow a plan that substitutes meal replacements for one or two meals a day. Your RDN can help you create this kind of weight loss plan without sacrificing nutrition.

Finding *Your* Balance

The **Daily Meal Patterns for Healthy Weight Loss** chart lists the number of servings you should aim to include from each food group each day, depending on your daily calorie level. Use this guide to make sure you eat a balanced diet as you lose weight.

Daily Meal Patterns for Healthy Weight Loss

Food Group	DAILY CALORIE TARGET					Serving Information
	1,200 Calories	1,400 Calories	1,600 Calories	1,800 Calories	2,000 Calories	
Fruits	1 cup	1½ cups	1½ cups	1½ cups	2 cups	1 cup is 1 cup fresh or frozen fruit (raw or cooked) or 1 cup canned, unsweetened fruit.
Vegetables	1½ cups	1½ cups	2 cups	2½ cups	2½ cups	1 cup equals 1 cup raw or cooked vegetables or 2 cups leafy salad greens.
Grains	4 ounce-equivalents	5 ounce-equivalents	5 ounce-equivalents	6 ounce-equivalents	6 ounce-equivalents	1 ounce-equivalent for grains is one 1-ounce slice bread; ½ cup cooked rice, pasta, or cereal; 1 tortilla (6-inch diameter); 1 pancake (5-inch diameter); or 1 ounce ready-to-eat cereal (about 1 cup cereal flakes).
Protein foods	3 ounce-equivalents	4 ounce-equivalents	5 ounce-equivalents	5 ounce-equivalents	5½ ounce-equivalents	1 ounce-equivalent for protein foods is 1 ounce lean meat, poultry, or seafood; 1 egg; 1 tablespoon peanut butter; or ½ ounce nuts or seeds. ¼ cup cooked beans or peas may also be counted as 1 ounce-equivalent.
Dairy	2½ cups	2½ cups	3 cups	3 cups	3 cups	1 cup of dairy is 1 cup milk, fortified soy beverage, or yogurt; 1½ ounces natural cheese (such as cheddar); or 2 ounces of processed cheese (such as American).

Source: Adapted from the US Department of Agriculture and US Department of Health and Human Services. *Dietary Guidelines for Americans, 2010.* http://health.gov/dietaryguidelines/dga2010/dietaryguidelines2010.pdf.

When Size Matters: Portion Control

When controlling calories, *how much* you eat is just as important to consider as what you eat. Portion sizes have exploded since the 1970s and have contributed to the great warping of American eating habits. A "small" soft drink has grown from 6 ounces to 20 ounces. A "snack-size" bag of chips used to contain 1 ounce; now, the typical bag weighs 3½ ounces. As portion sizes more than triple, so does calorie intake … and so do waistbands.

The reason that growing portion sizes are such a problem is that we tend to eat what is in front of us. Although humans are wired to eat for hunger, we often eat for many other reasons. For instance, certain cues (such as the time of day, the sight of food, or certain feelings) signal *when* to eat. Portion size has become a cue telling us *how much* to eat.

To understand the ways that portion sizes influence how much we eat, researchers at Cornell University conducted an experiment using "magical" bowls that secretly and imperceptibly refilled from the bottom. One group of subjects was served from a normal bowl and reported feeling satisfied after one serving. However, the group of subjects with the refilling bowls kept eating and eating. They denied feeling full because they perceived that they had eaten only half a bowl. The study, published in *Obesity Research,* revealed that we decide when to stop eating based on how much food is left on our plates or in our bowls.

In another Cornell University study, published in the *Journal of Nutrition Education and Behavior,* researchers gave subjects containers full of stale popcorn. Some subjects got a medium container, and they ate most of it. Others got a large container. They *also* ate most of it. Regardless of the portion, the subjects ate most of whatever size was put in front of them. And the popcorn wasn't even fresh! Sound familiar? It seems the subconscious mantra is "Have food, will eat."

Are You a Distracted Eater?

Multitasking is overrated, especially when it comes to eating. In this scurried and scattered race that is the American way of life, it's hard to take time to give our full attention to any single thing. Eating at your desk, while driving, or in front of the TV are examples of distracted or mindless eating, and when you are not paying attention, you can end up eating more food than you need. When you eat, limit distractions. Turn off the TV, sit at the dining table, eat slowly, and focus on each bite.

Because we rely on what we see to decide how much to eat, identifying appropriate portion sizes is an important and often overlooked factor in weight management. Here are some strategies you can use to keep your portions in check:

- **Use smaller plates, glasses, and serving utensils.** When we use bigger dishes, we tend to eat more food. Research has shown that using smaller plates, such as salad plates, decreases the amount of food people eat.

- **Measure and weigh foods**. When you make the commitment to weight loss, weigh and measure foods until you learn what various serving sizes look like. After a couple of weeks, you will start to recognize appropriate portions and may not need to be as rigid about measuring your foods. However, it is a good idea to spot-check yourself every now and then to be sure your portions haven't started creeping up in size. To learn serving sizes, you will need a set of dry-measuring cups, measuring spoons, a liquid-measuring cup, and a food scale. Once you have this equipment, you can simplify things a bit by measuring how much a certain glass, ladle, or bowl holds. Refer to **Be Size Wise** on page 21 for some tips about determining portion sizes.

- **Avoid "heaping" portions.** Some people "cheat" by measuring foods without precision, but those extra calories still show up on the scale!

- **Notice serving sizes on packaged foods.** The Nutrition Facts panel on a food label lists the number of calories per serving of the food in the package. The serving size is set by the food manufacturer and may not be the same as the portion you eat. (See Chapter 9.)

- **Be accurate when looking up nutrition information.** If you use a website or calorie book to look up the calorie information for a particular food—say, for example, a bran muffin—you may find it listed as having 180 calories. That amount may be accurate for a muffin that weighs about 2 ounces. But what if the muffin you purchase weighs 6 ounces (which is much more likely)? This muffin could have about 600 calories—420 calories more than the listed amount. This simple error could put you well over your daily calorie level and seriously impact your weight loss.

Be Size Wise: Useful Comparisons

A portion of:	Is the same size as:
3 ounces of meat or tofu	A deck of cards
1 cup of rice, lettuce, cereal, or other food	1 tennis ball or baseball
½ cup of food	1 regular light bulb
1 pancake	1 DVD
2 tablespoons peanut butter	1 golf ball

Fill 'er Up

8

Cutting back on calories may leave you feeling hungry as you adjust to new eating habits. If you can't concentrate over the sound of your stomach growling, try these strategies for feeling full:

- **Eat foods high in fiber.** High-fiber foods, such as whole grains, beans, and some fruits and vegetables, require more work to eat and provide more bulk than other more calorie-dense foods. In studies, people who ate high-fiber diets were less likely to be overweight and often reported eating fewer calories.
- **Eat foods high in water.** Water in foods adds volume, which can make foods more satisfying to your stomach *and* your mind. Compare, for instance, 15 fresh grapes versus 15 raisins. What's the crucial difference? The grapes have water, and the raisins do not. You can place the comparatively large grapes in a bowl and eat them one at a time, in 15 bites. In contrast, you could eat all 15 raisins in just one bite. If you are having a snack, which would be more satisfying? Fresh fruits and vegetables, which are high in both fiber and water content, are more filling and signal to your body that you have eaten and can get on with your day.
- **Eat less fat.** Remember our earlier calorie comparison of high-fat prime rib versus low-fat tilapia? Compared to carbohydrate or protein, fat provides more than twice as many calories per gram, so limiting fatty foods means you can eat more of other types of foods. For example, you can have 4 ounces of baked tilapia for the same number of calories as 1 ounce of prime rib. Two slices of bread have the same amount of calories as just half a biscuit made with shortening or butter. Do you get the idea?
- **Limit liquid calories.** When you drink liquids that contain calories, it's easy to go over your calorie budget. You can probably drink a cup of juice in a minute, but eating two pieces of fruit would take longer. Also, liquids don't stay in your

stomach as long as solid food, so the fruit will leave you feeling more satisfied than the juice. Cut back on sugary drinks (soft drinks, blended coffee or tea drinks, or packaged juice-flavored drinks), which are high in calories, and drink water instead. (If meal replacement drinks are part of your weight loss strategy, remember to discuss their use with your RDN, as mentioned on page 18.)

9 Examining Food Labels

Sample Nutrition Facts for a Package of Muffins

Nutrition Facts
Serving Size 1 muffin
Servings Per Container 2

Amount Per Serving

Calories 220	Calories from Fat 110

	% Daily Values*
Total Fat 12g	18%
Saturated Fat 6g	30%
Trans Fat 3g	
Cholesterol 0mg	0%
Sodium 330mg	14%
Total Carbohydrate 25g	8%
Dietary Fiber 0g	0%
Sugars 12g	
Protein 2g	4%

Vitamin A 2%	•	Calcium 4%
Iron 6%		

*Percent Daily Values are based on a 2,000 calorie diet. Your Daily Values may be higher or lower depending on your calorie needs.

		Calories	2,000	2,500
Total Fat	Less than		65g	80g
Sat Fat	Less than		20g	25g
Cholesterol	Less than		300mg	300mg
Sodium	Less than		2400mg	2400mg
Total Carbohydrate			300g	375g
Dietary Fiber			25g	30g

When buying packaged foods, you have probably noticed the Nutrition Facts panel. Manufacturers must provide this nutrition information on all packaged foods, with a few exceptions. Let's take a closer look at the sample label on this page. Notice that it gives you information about calories, fat, total carbohydrate, fiber, sugars, and protein that you can use for meal planning.

As you study labeling on food packages, keep in mind the following tips:

- **Look at the serving size.** Information is listed *per serving*, not per package. If you eat more than one serving, you need to do the math to determine your total calories and amounts of other nutrients, such as fat or fiber. The sample Nutrition Facts panel shown here is for a package of two blueberry muffins. It says there are 220 calories per serving and 2 servings per container. The whole package, then, has 440 calories. It is a good idea to think about these things before you buy a food item. If you know that you always eat the entire contents of a package, buying a container with fewer servings may be a better choice, even if it costs more.

- **Comparison shop.** Different brands or varieties of the same type of food, such as a muffin or cereal, may vary widely in calories and nutrition. Read the labels to determine the "best buy."

- **Watch out for marketing tricks.** Just because a food is labeled "light," "low fat," or "low sugar" doesn't mean it fits into your weight loss plan. Look at the calories per serving and serving size.

- **Decode the Daily Value.** The numbers in the % Daily Values column are based on a 2,000-calorie diet. If your meal plan contains fewer (or more) calories, these percentages won't reflect your needs. However, you can still use the numbers to compare similar foods and find out which one provides more or less of the listed nutrients per serving. For example, you could use the % Daily Values for total fat, protein, and calcium to help you choose between two brands of yogurt.

Dining Out

Dining out has become an integral part of the American way of life. It's easy to overdose on calories when eating out, but it's not inevitable. These tips will help you stick to your weight loss plan:

- **Look for nutrition information.** Most restaurant chains post calorie and nutrition information on their websites. Some print it on the menu, while others may be able to provide it upon request. Use this information to identify entrées that fit into your daily calorie budget.
- **Plan ahead.** Since many restaurants post menus online, you can come prepared with one or two healthy options already in mind. By deciding what you will order before you head out, you won't browse the menu and be tempted by other less healthy options. You can also plan to trim back on other meals that day to account for the extra calories you may consume at the restaurant.
- **Look for key words in the descriptions.** When you can't locate nutrition information, look for clues in the menu descriptions of various dishes. Words such as *baked*, *grilled*, *roasted*, *broiled*, or *steamed* are likely lower-calorie options than *sautéed*, *fried*, *creamed*, *crispy*, or *battered*.
- **Skip the bread basket.** If bread shows up at your table, ask the server to take it away so you aren't tempted.
- **Start with a salad.** Fill up on a low-calorie option, such as a garden salad or a broth-based soup.
- **Ask for modifications.** When an entrée comes with a high-calorie side dish, like fries, ask your server if you can substitute fresh fruit or steamed vegetables, even if they aren't on the menu. Request that your entrée come without butter, cheese, sour cream, mayonnaise, or bacon, which are high in calories. Also ask for sauces and salad dressings on the side so you can control how much of these often high-calorie condiments you use.
- **Take half your meal home.** To keep your portions in check, ask your server to bring a to-go container with the meal. Put half of your meal in the container right away.
- **Choose a low-calorie beverage.** Skip the soda. Instead, order unsweetened ice tea or water with lemon.

Now take a few minutes to go online and look for the nutrition information for your favorite restaurants. How many calories are in your favorite dishes? Can you identify a couple of lower-calorie options?

11 Map Out Your Course

When traveling, it is difficult to map out a course when you don't have a destination in mind. Similarly, it's difficult to embark on a life-changing program without knowing what goals you want to achieve. A goal is like a destination—when you have a specific goal, you can map out a course to reach it.

Goals serve other functions, too. They help you make a commitment to change, and they help you stay focused on the direction you want to head.

Set SMARTER Goals

Perhaps you've set goals in the past that you haven't been able to meet. Don't despair! It is very likely that the goal was faulty—not you. To set yourself on the path to success, follow the SMARTER goals guidelines.

Goals should be:

- **Specific:** Be clear about what you want. If want to lose weight, state exactly how many pounds you want to lose. If you want to eat more healthfully, state specifically how you will improve your eating habits. For example, "I will keep to a limit of 1,400 calories a day" is more specific than "I will watch what I eat."
- **Measurable:** Make your goal something you can measure. Continuing with the example above, you could track the calories you consume to know whether you are meeting your goal.
- **Achievable:** Focus on behaviors you can control. For instance, you can't directly control how much weight you will lose this week, because you may retain fluid one day or hit a plateau one month. However, you can control the behaviors that lead to weight loss, such as eating a set number of calories and doing physical activity. So, instead of stating "My goal is to lose 2 pounds this week," phrase your goal as "This week, I will consume no more than 1,400 calories per day."
- **Realistic:** Suppose you work full time, raise a family, go to school, and have never liked running. Training to complete a marathon 6 months from now may not be an achievable goal for you. Being realistic means setting a goal that is challenging, but not overwhelming, so you can experience success and build confidence in your ability to conquer bigger challenges.
- **Time-bound:** Setting specific start and end dates for your goal will help you commit to a timeframe and get off the "I'll start on Monday" track.
- **Evaluated:** Goals are evolving and ongoing. Look at your goals periodically and assess how you are doing. If you are running into roadblocks, identify the obstacles. For example, let's say your goal is to jog three mornings a week before work. At the end of the week, you realize that you kept hitting the snooze button instead of going for that run. It may be time to evaluate your goal. You may need a strategy to help you get out of bed in the morning, such as moving the alarm clock to the

other side of the room. You may need to consider a different form of exercise that inspires you more. Whatever you do, do not assume that you are faulty. If you are having trouble reaching a particular goal, it is the goal that may be faulty and you may need to revise it.

- **Rewarded:** Celebrate successes! Acknowledge your achievements, whether by letting yourself feel proud, by treating yourself to something nice, or by marking a check on your progress sheet. (For reward ideas, see Chapter 19: No-Calorie Treats and Rewards.)

SMARTER Goal Setting Worksheet

My Goal: _____

Specific	What actions will I take to reach my goal?
Measurable	What will I use to track my progress (e.g., food records, weigh-ins and measurements, physical activity records)?
Achievable	What behaviors that I can control will help me reach this goal?
Realistic	Is this goal something I can see myself accomplishing? How does this fit in with my life?
Time-bound	By what date will I reach my goal? What other milestones would I like to set?
Evaluated	What questions can I ask to evaluate my progress?
Rewarded	How will I reward myself?

Sticking to Your Goals

Now that you've crafted a SMARTER goal, here are some tips to help you stay committed:

- Write down your goal and post it in places you will see several times a day, such as the bathroom mirror, your computer monitor, a cupboard, or your dashboard.
- Set reminders on your smart phone.
- Tell your family, friends, and coworkers what your goal is. You'll remember it whenever you run into them!
- Write out a contract. Having a written and signed document can feel more compelling.
- Use the Goal Record Sheet (Appendix 3) to check off each day that you accomplish your goals. Seeing the checkmarks stack up is very motivating!

12 Put It in Writing! Self-Monitoring

Sandy has a pretty good idea of what she ate yesterday: coffee, cereal, and milk for breakfast; a sandwich with baked chips for lunch; and fish, potatoes, and peas for dinner. Oh, and a dish of ice cream for a snack. The following box shows Sandy's estimate of the number of calories she ate.

Sandy's Estimated Calories	
Breakfast:	Coffee: 0 1 cup cereal: 100 ½ cup milk: 50
Lunch:	2 slices of bread: 150 Turkey: 150 Baked chips: 100
Dinner:	Fish: 150 Potatoes: 75 Peas: 50
Snacks:	Ice cream: 175
	Total calories: 1,000

Based on this estimate, it just doesn't seem fair: Why can't Sandy lose weight if she's eating only 1,000 calories per day? However, Sandy, like most people, tends to underestimate her portions and the number of calories in the foods she eats. She tends to forget or overlook foods, too. If she had measured portions, recorded every bite, and looked up accurate calorie information, she would have come up with very different results (see box at right).

No wonder Sandy isn't losing weight! The point is, when you carefully record information, you get an honest, realistic picture of what you are eating. This process helps you in many ways.

The Advantages of Keeping Food Records

Keeping a detailed daily record of what you eat has many advantages:

Sandy's Actual Calories	
Breakfast:	12-ounce coffee: 0
	2 tablespoons fat-free milk: 10
	2 teaspoons sugar: 30
	1½ cups cereal: 165
	1 cup fat-free milk: 90
Lunch:	2 slices of bread: 200
	4½ ounces deli turkey: 150
	1 tablespoon mayonnaise: 95
	1½ cups baked potato chips: 240
Dinner:	6 ounces baked white fish: 160
	6-ounce baked potato: 160
	2 tablespoons butter: 200
	½ cup peas with 1 teaspoon butter: 110
	12-ounce cola: 150
Snacks:	1 cup chocolate ice cream: 330
	½ chocolate chip cookie: 55
	1 package peanut butter crackers: 220
	12-ounce coffee with 2 tablespoons cream and 2 teaspoons sugar: 70
Total calories: 2,435	

1. **Noting the details on food records allows you to see the math.** It is very easy to underestimate how many calories you eat and wonder why you aren't losing weight. You might get discouraged and think that you simply can't change your weight. But recording exactly how many calories you eat may reveal that your obstacle simply comes down to numbers.

2. **Reviewing food records helps you identify opportunities for improvement.** In reviewing your food record for the day, you might find easy ways to cut calories. For instance, skipping the butter on your toast, using mustard instead of mayonnaise, and choosing yogurt instead of ice cream for an evening snack could cut more than 600 calories!

3. **Tracking every bite in food records reveals how "nibbling" adds up.** It's easy to eat without thinking: a piece of a cookie, some hard candy, and a little handful of chips. But these extra nibbles really add up over the course of the day, and a food record will show you just how many extra calories you're consuming.

4. **Keeping food records enables you to confront your choices by connecting food to consequences.** When you know that you have to add a food to your record, you have a chance to think about the consequences and decide whether eating it is something you really want to do after all. For example, if you know you have to write down a 220-calorie package of peanut butter crackers, you might choose baby carrots instead.

5. **Reflecting on your food records helps you see your progress toward meeting your goals.** If you get discouraged, you can look back over past food records to remind yourself where you started and how far you have come. You also can use successful days or weeks as a model for future behavior. For instance, if you went to a wedding in the past and made good food choices, you can review that day's record in preparation for an upcoming wedding.

6. **Maintaining food records helps you learn how many calories are in the foods you eat.** As you become familiar with calorie contents and portion sizes, you will eventually be able to keep records in less time and make choices that fall within your calorie budget without needing to look up nutrition information or weigh and measure foods.

7. **Evaluating food records helps you identify behavior patterns that lead to success or failure.** Do you always overeat on days when you are stressed or feeling down? Do particular people influence your eating patterns? Does the time of day make an impact on how much you eat? Tracking the circumstances around when and what you eat (such as mood, location, and company) helps you spot trends so you can reinforce positive behaviors and improve troublesome ones. You may decide that you need to avoid a certain person while you are trying to lose weight or that you need to develop some healthy ways to cope with emotions.

Where to Find the Calorie Information for Food Records

You've learned how to find calories per serving by reading food labels. You've also learned that many chain restaurants provide calorie counts on their menus, websites, or upon request. In addition, you can find reliable calorie and nutrition information for tens of thousands of foods by using online resources and smart phone apps. (See Appendix 2 for a list of digital resources.) There are a number of print books as well, such as the pocket-sized *The Calorie King Calorie, Fat, & Carbohydrate Counter 2014* (Family Health Publications; 2013).

Guidelines for Keeping Food Records

Many studies have shown that keeping food records is strongly associated with success in weight loss. Keeping records, however, can be challenging. It is quite a bit of work, especially at first, and it may diminish the pleasures of eating—for example, you may not experience that devious sense of fun that goes with eating a banana split when you have to calculate and confront the fact that it has 1,500 calories. Putting in a little time and effort, though, will keep you focused on your choices today and make getting on the scale a little easier tomorrow. The following guidelines will help you get started:

1. **Decide where you will record your food.** If you prefer to keep track electronically, there are many reliable and user-friendly websites and apps to help you. (See Appendix 2: Digital Resources.) You simply search for the foods you eat, enter the portion, and these tools do the math for you. These resources typically include information about packaged and restaurant foods, making tracking convenient. However, some may not allow you to track other factors that can be important in identifying triggers, such as your mood or location while eating. If you prefer pen and paper, find a small notebook that you can carry with you and access easily. The pages should have room to fit records for a full day on one sheet. That way, when you analyze the records, you won't have to flip pages. The notebook should also have enough pages for a week or several weeks of records. Do not keep your records on loose sheets of paper, which can easily get shuffled or lost.

2. **Record each food as you eat it.** Keep track of at least the food, its portion size, and the number of calories. You may also find it useful to note the people you are with, where you eat, your mood, and how hungry you feel before you eat. (See **Sandy's Sample Food Record** on page 29 for ideas.) If you do not know the

number of calories in a certain food while you are eating it, look it up as soon as you have access to a calorie book.

3. **Learn portion sizes so you can record them accurately.** How much you eat is as important as what you eat. At first, you will need to weigh and measure everything to determine accurately what you are eating. As you become more experienced, you will know portion sizes just by looking at a food. (Even then, it is a good idea to spot-check yourself for accuracy.)

4. **Keep a running total so that you know at all times where you stand in your "calorie budget."** Doing so allows you to be proactive—not reactive—regarding your food choices. Watching the calories add up every time you eat can be painful, but it also helps you see where you stand.

Sandy's Sample Food Record

TODAY'S DATE: JUNE 6, 2014

Time	Food and Portion Size	Calories	Hunger (0 = Not at all hungry; 5 = Extremely hungry)	Mood	With	Where	Running Calorie Total
7:00 A.M.	3-ounce bagel	225	5	Stressed	Self	Kitchen table	270
	2 teaspoons grape jelly	35					
	Coffee	0					
	2 teaspoons nonfat milk	10					
8:30 A.M.	12-ounce coffee	0	0	Happy	Self	Desk	285
	2 teaspoons whole milk	15					
12:00 P.M.	2 cups garden salad	10	5	Happy	Molly		775
	2 tablespoons fat-free ranch salad dressing	30					
	4-ounce blueberry muffin	400					
	2 cups coffee	0					
	2 individual-sized containers half-and-half	50					
3:00 P.M.	1 ounce pretzels	100	4	Tired	Self	Desk	1,010
	1-ounce chocolate chip cookie	135					
6:00 P.M.	3-ounce hamburger	225	5	Lonely	Self	Kitchen table	1,655
	2 ounces white bread	150					
	1 tablespoon ketchup	30					
	½ cup potato salad	130					
	3 ounces wine	110					
8:30 P.M.	1 cup sugar-free hot chocolate	50	1	Tired	Self	Couch	1,840
	1-ounce peanut butter cookie	135					

Total Daily Calories: 1,840
Physical Activity: 1 hour aerobics (465 calories burned)
Weekly weight: 165 pounds (before breakfast)

Using Food Records

Now let's play detective. Look at Sandy's sample food record. Suppose she needs to take in about 1,800 calories per day to maintain her weight if she does not exercise. Her goal is to take in 1,400 calories per day. She went over this goal by 440 calories. By looking at her records, let's see if we can find out where she ran into trouble.

Notice that Sandy ate a third of her total calories at dinner. What may have caused her to overeat?

_____

_____

_____

Perhaps Sandy was overly hungry by the time she got home. Feeling lonely may have also contributed to how much she ate.

Now that you have considered causes for Sandy's overeating, what are some strategies she could apply to be more successful tomorrow?

_____

_____

_____

Sandy was very hungry and felt lonely at dinner time. Maybe if she had an apple on the way home, planned a low-calorie meal, and had a friend over, she would eat a lighter dinner. She also could have eaten a more balanced breakfast and lunch. Maybe then she would not have wanted the snacks in the afternoon.

Now use what you have learned about calories and nutrition to evaluate Sandy's food choices. What choices could she have made to eat fewer calories and make food choices that fit her meal pattern for healthy weight loss? (For meal patterns, see the chart on page 19.)

_____

_____

_____

Did you notice that Sandy did not eat any fruit or dairy products (except the milk in her coffee), and did not have enough servings from the protein group? Instead of a blueberry muffin at lunch, she could have chosen 1 cup of fat-free yogurt (a dairy food with protein), saving about 300 calories. In the afternoon, she could have replaced cookies with a piece of fruit.

This exercise should give you an idea as to how to analyze your own food records to identify areas of improvement.

Track Your Progress: Weights and Measurements

13

In addition to keeping track of your food, keep a record of your weight and body measurements so you can see your progress. Here are some basic guidelines to follow:

1. **Weigh yourself once a week**. People who check their weight at least weekly tend to maintain weight change. Be aware that small daily weight fluctuations are typical. Therefore, weekly weigh-ins track change more accurately and address weight gain promptly.

2. **Always weigh yourself first thing in the morning, before you eat or drink anything.** At this time of the day, you will obtain the most accurate weight. If you drink 16 ounces of water and then weigh yourself a half hour later, you will weigh 1 pound more, because of that extra pound of fluid in your body.

3. **Always weigh yourself on the same scale.** Some scales show lighter or heavier weights than others, so it's best to use the same scale for consistency.

4. **Measure the distances around your upper arms, hips, neck, and thighs.** As you start exercising, you may add muscle while you lose fat. Because muscle is denser than fat, 1 pound of muscle takes up less space than 1 pound of fat. Therefore, your measurements will shrink and your pants may fit looser, even if the scale doesn't show much of a change. You can also track blood sugar (glucose) and blood pressure levels as additional indicators of progress.

5. **Measure your body fat percentage.** You may wish to contact a trainer at a local gym to see if he or she can periodically measure your body fat. These measurements provide objective information about the results of your program.

14 Move It and Lose It! Physical Activity

Sedentary lifestyles are a key reason for the obesity epidemic in the United States and other Western nations. Modern conveniences have reduced the amount of activity we get. Many of us sit in our cars for long commutes to jobs that require 8 hours of sitting a day. According to some health experts, sitting is as detrimental to our health as smoking. So it's important to get up and start moving.

Physical activity burns calories, improves your mindset, and benefits your health. Just as important, it helps you to develop the habits that will help keep you at a healthier weight for life.

Benefits of Getting Up and Moving

Better sleep
Better mood
Improved blood sugar (glucose) control
Stronger bones and joints
Self-confidence
Improved blood pressure
Stronger heart

You might be thinking, "I would be more active if my knees and back didn't hurt me," or "if I didn't get winded climbing the stairs," or "if I didn't feel like everyone was staring at me." Perhaps you're thinking, "People must really enjoy moving to do it regularly, but that's just not me." When you equate exercise with pain, boredom, failure, or humiliation, it makes sense that you would have a distaste for physical activity. Many people start out there. But you can create a different relationship with physical activity.

Here are some statements from people who had once been limited by extreme obesity:

- "I completed a half marathon!" —Judy K.
- "I love spinning! It's so fun and it's a great workout." —Madeleine M.
- "My daughter and I are training for a 10K." —Dwayne C.
- "I climbed Mount Rainier last weekend." —Mark H.

These people weren't climbing Mount Rainier or training for a 10K when they were 100 or 200 pounds overweight. But, as they began to lose weight and started exercising, new possibilities arose. Who would have thought they would end up loving physical activity? Certainly not them!

Here are some facts that may help you think differently about physical activity:

- Any amount of activity is better than no activity.
- You can start where you are and build from there.
- You can get your activity in brief (10-minute) increments.
- Walking briskly is a moderate activity that most people can safely do.
- You can use exercise DVDs or online videos in the privacy of your home.

What are some obstacles that have prevented you from getting started with physical activity? Use the following space to list them (for example, "I have no time," "I hurt my foot," or "I'm too tired when I get home"). Then counter each obstacle with possible solutions:

Obstacles	Solutions
Example: I have knee pain	Ask doctor about physical therapy. Try water aerobics.

Confronting your obstacles is a great start! Now consider this: What if you could walk just 10 minutes more each day? Even 10 minutes makes a difference. The smallest amount of activity changes your body. You become a little bit stronger. Your heart gets a little more efficient. Your lungs use oxygen a little bit better. Soon you feel capable of adding a little bit more, and your body adapts, getting stronger still. As you lose weight from moving a little and especially from following a healthy, calorie-restricted eating plan, the stress on your knees, back, and heart decreases. Moving begins to get easier. You will soon find yourself saying, "I can walk upstairs without stopping for air!" and "I just walked a mile!" You are seeing results.

What Good Will 10 Minutes Do? A Lot!

Exercising for 10 minutes two or three times a week is an excellent way to develop the habit of physical activity. It is hard not to find 10 minutes to get moving, even on the busiest days.
While 10 minutes of activity a day may not have a big impact on your weight, being active 10 minutes a day consistently over a lifetime will provide a more positive outcome than exercising 2 hours a day and burning out after 6 weeks.
  Studies have found that three 10-minute bouts of physical activity have the same positive effects on health as a single 30-minute bout.

Types of Physical Activity

Physical activity includes aerobic activity, muscle strengthening, and flexibility exercises. Each type of activity is important and offers different health benefits.

Aerobic Activity

Aerobic exercise (or "cardio") is any activity that uses your large muscles to get your heart beating faster. Examples include brisk walking, cycling, dancing, playing basketball, or heavy gardening. Research has repeatedly shown that aerobic activity is associated with successful long-term weight loss.

If you can, start with at least 150 minutes of activity per week (which equates to 30 minutes a day, 5 days a week), and gradually work up to more as you are able. Research shows that 225 to 420 minutes per week is optimal for weight loss. Once you reach your weight loss goal, aim for 200 to 300 minutes of activity per week to keep the weight off.

Walking is a popular type of moderate activity. Walking 30 minutes a day can burn about 100 or 200 calories, depending on your weight and pace. If you walk 30 minutes a day for 5 days a week, your walks can burn 500 to 1,000 calories!

Muscle Strengthening Activity

You can increase muscle strength with resistance exercises, such as weight training, using elastic bands, and exercises that use your own weight, such as pushups. Follow these guidelines to incorporate resistance training into your physical activity plan:

- Do some resistance training 2 days a week.
- Do exercises for each muscle group, including the legs, hips, back, abdomen, arms, shoulders, and chest.
- A "set" is 8 to 12 repetitions (or "reps") of an exercise. Do 1 to 2 sets of each exercise during each episode of resistance training.
- The last rep of each set should be difficult, but not so hard that you can't maintain proper form.

Although resistance exercises build and tone muscles, they will not get rid of fat in specific areas, such as the stomach. Only overall fat loss can do that, which you achieve by burning more calories than you consume.

Flexibility Exercises

Increasing your flexibility by stretching reduces the risk of injury and improves your range of motion. Yoga is one way to increase your flexibility, and classes are offered through many gyms and community centers.

Safety Factors for an Active Life

Before beginning a physical activity program, review the following safety factors. If any of them apply to you, check with your doctor to see whether increasing activity is safe:

- You have a chronic disease, such as diabetes or asthma.
- You have high blood pressure, high cholesterol, or a personal or family history of heart disease.
- You are pregnant.
- You smoke.
- You have other concerns about exercise and your health.
- You are a man older than 40 or woman older than 50 (prior to starting a vigorous activity program).

For assistance in starting a safe and effective physical activity program, seek professional assistance through a certified personal trainer, an exercise physiologist, or a licensed physical therapist. Reputable certification organizations include the American College of Sports Medicine and the American Council on Exercise.

Reasons to Stop Exercising Immediately

Stop exercising and seek medical attention immediately if you:

- Have pain, tightness, or pressure in your chest, neck, shoulder, or arm.
- Feel dizzy or sick.
- Break out in a cold sweat.
- Have muscle cramps.
- Are extremely short of breath.
- Feel pain in your joints, feet, ankles, or legs.

Keeping Activity Comfortable

You are probably more likely to stick with a physical activity program if you feel as good as possible while you are active. These tips can help improve your exercise experience:

- Warm up and cool down.
- Stretch after exercise.
- Don't overdo it. Start slowly and build time and intensity.
- Invest in good shoes, and replace them often!
- Wear comfortable, loose-fitting clothes.

For additional suggestions and information, visit the Publications page at the Weight-Control Information Network (www.win.niddk.nih.gov) and click *Active at Any Size*.

Sticking with the Program

Remember, a physical activity program is a marathon, not a sprint, and you want to pace yourself for the long haul. Here are some tried-and-true steps for successfully starting and maintaining a workout regimen:

- **Use the buddy system.** Find a partner who will commit to a regular physical activity program with you, or hire a reputable, certified trainer to hold you accountable.
- **Choose activities that suit your interests and your needs.** Find activities that you enjoy. If you hate exercising indoors, then a gym probably isn't for you but perhaps there's a park nearby with trails for hiking or biking. If you have bad knees, running may be out of the question but walking or elliptical training could be options.
- **Be realistic.** You will not be able to lose 20 pounds in a month. Your waist will not go from 40 inches to 25 inches in 2 months. Even if you are making tremendous progress, you may end up discouraged if your activity plan doesn't meet your impossible expectations. Turn to Chapter 11: Map Out Your Course to review how to set SMARTER goals that will lead you to success.
- **Write up a contract stating your plan.** Then sign it with one of your supporters.

- **Celebrate small successes.** Establish a nonfood reward system to celebrate each small goal you achieve along the way. See Chapter 19: No-Calorie Treats and Rewards for ideas.
- **Use an activity tracker or a pedometer.** Wearable activity trackers, smart phone apps, and pedometers are great ways to encourage activity and motivate you to meet goals by tracking your daily movement. Work up to at least 10,000 steps a day.
- **Obtain body measurements at regular time intervals** (such as each month). Even though you are burning fat through activity, you may actually gain some weight because muscle is denser than fat. Therefore, taking body measurements may show encouraging results (like a smaller waist) even when the scale does not, and these changes can help motivate you to keep going. Turn to Chapter 13: Track Your Progress for guidance on taking measurements.

Now take a moment to write down types of physical activities you enjoy:

_____

_____

In the past, what has helped you stick with a physical activity plan?

_____

_____

_____

_____

What got in the way?

_____

_____

_____

What are some strategies you can use to prevent those roadblocks from interfering with your plan?

_____

_____

_____

Revving Up Your Daily Routine

In addition to having a formal physical activity plan, you can burn extra calories by increasing your routine daily activity. For instance, get up to change the television channel, park far away from your destination, take the stairs, and walk to a coworker's desk instead of using the telephone. Although they may not seem like much, these little activities add up.

Can you list five simple ways to increase daily activity in your life?

1. _____

2. _____

3. _____

4. _____

5. _____

Gaining Support

15

Research has shown that people who have support are more successful at weight loss and weight maintenance. Support can take a variety of forms and come from many sources. It can be as simple as someone congratulating you on your weight loss or acknowledging that you stuck to your commitment during a tough time. Support can also be more involved. For instance, perhaps your spouse will need to stop bringing home doughnuts or agree to keep high-calorie foods hidden.

Not everyone can get the support he or she needs at home. Luckily, outside sources of support are also available. Weight loss groups (such as Weight Watchers, TOPS Club, or Overeaters Anonymous), weight loss counselors, and RDNs are reputable sources of support. You may also have good friends who can help you. Think about which individuals or groups you can turn to for support. List them here:

_____

_____

It can be difficult to ask for help, or to articulate exactly what you need from your supporters. Because support is so important in weight loss success, the following sections will help you evaluate your obstacles and develop a plan to overcome them.

Evaluate Your Obstacles

Fear of criticism, feeling undeserving, or fear of being a burden are just a few reasons that asking for support can be difficult. Reflect on your own weight loss efforts. Have you ever wanted someone's help but did not let that person know? Why didn't you say anything?

_____

_____

Sometimes, the behaviors of family, friends, coworkers, and others do not support your weight loss efforts. For example, Lou notes, "When my friends and I get together, they always want to go to the pizza place that doesn't have a salad bar. I want to spend time with these friends, but there isn't anything healthy to eat and I end up going over my daily calorie budget." Write an example of unsupportive behavior from your own experience.

_____

_____

_____

Now think about some ways in which your friends, family, coworkers, or others *can* support you. (For example, "I could ask my friends to dine out at places that offer low-calorie foods.")

_____

_____

_____

_____

Communicate Your Needs

Once you become open to asking for support and have determined the kinds of help you need, you can communicate your needs to others. This step is hard for many people, so here are some pointers:

- **Use "I" statements.** Avoid putting others on the defensive. For instance, imagine you told your spouse, "You keep eating fattening foods in front of me, which makes me go off my eating plan." It would sound like you were blaming your spouse, and that may invite an argument instead of a willingness to help. By saying instead, "I have a difficult time resisting fattening foods when they are around me," you take ownership for the reason you are struggling. Think of an "I" statement that defines a problem that jeopardizes your weight loss efforts.

_____

_____

- **Let others know how they can help you.** To continue with our example, you might say, "It would help me if you would avoid eating fattening foods in front of me, either by eating them before you come home or by letting me know so that I can leave the room." Write down a statement that explains how the other person can help you overcome the problem you've identified in your own life.

_____

_____

- **Do not assume that people intuitively know how to help you.** You must let each person know what you need.
- **Do not assume that saying something once is adequate.** Because the problem is yours, it is more important to you and is likely to be on your mind. Other people may sincerely want to help, but they may need you to remind them—perhaps more than once.
- **Consider a support group.** If you are not able to get support from the people around you, an outside support group may be your best option.
- **Take ownership.** Even if you have a great support base, weight loss is still ultimately up to you, and solving problems remains your responsibility.

Role-Playing Activity

Some people say that losing weight is the hardest thing they ever tried to do. Asking for support is a big step toward finding success. You may find it helpful to practice using some of the tools you have learned in this chapter to prepare for real life situations.

Find a person you trust, such as a friend, significant other, or therapist. Ask this person to play the part of someone who presents a challenge to your weight loss, such as a family member who pushes food on you. Practice asserting yourself by expressing your needs without putting others on the defensive. It may be helpful to write down what you want to say, although you do not have to use what you have written when you role-play. Going through the motions can be a powerful tool in helping you in real situations.

16 Get Trigger Happy

Have you heard of Pavlov's dogs? Pavlov was a scientist who studied why dogs salivate when they are given food. In one experiment, he rang a bell every time the dogs were fed. After a while, the dogs associated the sound of the bell with feeding time, and their mouths would water when they heard the bell, even when there was no food. The bell triggered the same response as the presence of food. People learn to make these kinds of associations, too, and the triggers can lead to desired or undesired behaviors.

Any number of things can trigger behaviors: sights and smells, places, people, moods, package sizes of food items, the time of day, or certain activities. Perhaps you feel pulled like steel to a magnet when you pass a vending machine. Perhaps your hand automatically reaches for the chips when you're in front of the TV. If you use your food records to track your mood, the location, and your companions each time you eat, you can identify possible triggers for your eating behaviors. If you understand what factors trigger undesirable behaviors, you can develop strategies to eliminate the triggers or learn a new response to them.

Pat, for instance, knew that social gatherings were a trigger that led her to overeat. She was nervous about her grandchild's birthday party, which she was hosting in a week. Pat prepared for success in several ways. First, she made a commitment to stick to her goals during the party. Then she came up with a plan: She decided to prepare a main dish that she didn't like but that the family really liked—in this case, a beef roast—and cook plenty of vegetables so that there would be low-calorie foods to eat. She also decided that she would bake a cake that wasn't a favorite of hers. Finally, to make sure she wouldn't feel deprived, she got herself a treat that would fit into her plan.

What triggers undesirable behaviors in your life?

_____

_____

_____

_____

Not all triggers lead to negative behaviors. Some lead to positive responses. For example, a conversation with a particularly active friend may inspire you to work out. Can you identify positive triggers in your life?

_____

_____

_____

_____

Once you know what triggers lead to undesirable behaviors, you can develop strategies to remove them. Here are some suggestions:

- If the sight of food triggers your desire to eat, ask the people you live with to hide tempting snacks or store leftovers in opaque containers.
- Keep your pantry free of high-calorie foods, such as chips and cookies. If you want to indulge, buy a single-serving container.
- Avoid the cookie, snack, and bakery aisles at the grocery store.
- If you can't resist the vending machine, stop bringing change or small bills to work.
- Avoid watching cooking shows.
- Display a photo of a reward you plan to give yourself after achieving a goal. It will remind you to resist giving in to undesirable behaviors.

You can also learn to develop desirable responses by adding positive triggers. For example:

- Place easy-to-eat vegetables in your line of vision in the refrigerator.
- Put on your walking shoes to trigger the desire to go for a walk.
- Have healthy snacks at your desk.
- Spend time with supportive people with healthy lifestyles.
- Before going to bed, put exercise clothes out for the morning.

Another way to deal with triggers is to teach yourself different responses that replace undesirable behaviors with desirable ones. For example, if you know that the smell of movie theater popcorn is a trigger, bring a low-calorie snack to enjoy instead.

What are new behaviors you can learn to overcome negative triggers?

_____

_____

_____

_____

The Chains That Bind You: Breaking Your Behavior Chains

Have you ever found yourself looking into an empty ice cream carton, wondering how you let this happen again? You may not realize that an entire series of behaviors led to this undesirable outcome. Like the links of a chain, behaviors are linked together. And as the saying goes, "A chain is only as strong as its weakest link." To break a behavior chain, break it down into a series of behaviors and identify the "weakest link."

Let's take a look at an example, and then you can practice finding the weak links in a behavior chain you would like to break.

Every night on his way home from work, Greg automatically stops at the ice cream shop and buys a sundae. He knows that the sundae has 500 calories, and that it doesn't fit into his daily calorie budget. He has decided several times that he would stop this habit, but every day at 5:10 P.M., there he is, ordering a sundae.

Let's break Greg's behavior down into steps. Any of these steps may be a "weak link" that Greg can break, thereby avoiding that seemingly fateful sundae stop. Therefore, let's identify an alternative behavior for each step.

1. **Greg leaves work.** He will still leave work at the end of the day, but perhaps he can bring an apple for the trip home.

2. **Greg drives down Food Boulevard.** Can he drive down a different street—one that doesn't have as many food joints?

3. **Greg sees Iggy's Ice Cream Parlor.** Can he keep his eyes on the road and not look around as much?

4. **Greg thinks about ice cream.** When he starts to think of ice cream, can he divert his thoughts to something else, such as his plans for the weekend?

5. **Greg's mouth waters.** If he doesn't see or think about ice cream, he won't have this problem.

6. **Greg pulls into the parking lot.** Can he drive in the far lane so that it is not as easy to turn into Iggy's?

7. **Greg stops the car.** Can he let the car idle for 5 minutes to give himself a little cooling-off time? Can he phone a friend?

8. **Greg goes inside.** Can he commit to walking around the building first (and thus have more cooling-off time)?

9. **Greg orders a sundae.** Is there anything with fewer calories that he can order?

10. **Greg eats the sundae.** Can Greg save some calories from that day's budget so he can afford the sundae? Or can he eat a few bites and toss the rest?

Do you get the idea? Now identify a behavior that is interfering with your weight loss goals, and break it into individual steps and solutions.

Behavior I would like to change:

_____

_____

Step 1 in the behavior chain: _____

Solution: _____

Step 2: _____

Solution: _____

Step 3: _____

Solution: _____

Step 4: _____

Solution: _____

Step 5: _____

Solution: _____

Step 6: _____

Solution: _____

Have Faith...in Yourself   18

In the 1970s, the psychologist Martin Seligman conducted an experiment in which two groups of dogs were placed in cages and given an electrical shock. One group of dogs was given a way to escape, and they quickly learned that they would avoid the shock by jumping over a wall. The other group of dogs did not initially have a way to escape the shock. After a while, this group was also given the opportunity to escape, but the dogs continued to just sit there and endure the shock. Seligman called this behavior _learned helplessness_—once the dogs learned that they could not escape, they did not act, even after the circumstances changed.

People who have failed at weight loss efforts in the past may experience learned help-lessness. Many fad diets make claims such as "lose 10 pounds in a week," "eat all you want and still lose weight," or "lose weight by eating only grapefruit and cabbage soup—guaranteed!" However, what the creators of these diets don't tell you is that it takes the will of Hercules to stick to them for any length of time. If you fail repeatedly at weight loss, you may learn to believe that you cannot lose weight under any circumstances. In reality, however, it is often the approach to weight loss that is the problem, and not you.

Instead of giving up, examine your past defeats and learn from them so you can move forward with confidence. This is easier said than done. If you are feeling helpless, use the strategies in this chapter to regain your confidence and the belief you can change.

Set Realistic Goals

Nothing breeds success like success. If you doubt your ability to lose weight and live a healthy lifestyle, start fresh by setting small, progressive goals based on an honest appraisal of where and who you are. In this way, you can learn what success feels like, and build from there. Even a small success will help you learn to believe in your abilities, making you more confident and more likely to reach your next goal. (For more about setting goals, review Chapter 11: Map Out Your Course.)

Practice Self-Affirmations

In addition to past failures, the things that you and others say about you affect your self-image. If you hear a particular message often enough, you start to believe it. If the message is positive, you develop a positive self-image. If the message is negative, you develop a negative self-image. Imagine two hungry dogs, one mean and one nice. If you feed only the mean dog, he grows stronger while the nice dog gets weaker. If you feed only the nice dog, he gets stronger while the mean dog gets weaker. In the same way, you can choose which parts of your self-image to feed. To make your positive self-image stronger and your negative self-image weaker, feed yourself only positive messages (self-affirmations).

What are some negative messages you say or hear about yourself?

_____

_____

_____

_____

What are some positive messages or self-affirmations you can tell yourself instead?

_____

_____

_____

_____

Display these affirmations in a few places, just as you did with your goals, so you remember to repeat them often. When you catch yourself making negative comments about your ability to lose weight or about your self-worth, challenge them with positive thoughts. Even if you don't believe these affirmations at first, trust the process and stick with it. Eventually you will begin to believe them.

Find Role Models

Kids aren't the only ones who need good role models! Humans of every age often absorb the behaviors of those around them, so it's wise to spend time with people who embody the mindset you want to have. For instance, you can learn how to handle difficult situations by observing how a positive role model or a life coach handles them.

Visualize Desired Outcomes

You can also be your own role model, in a sense, by imagining yourself achieving the outcome you want—and expect! To use this technique (which sports psychologists call visualizing), picture a challenging situation in vivid detail: Where are you? What is happening? Who is with you? What are they doing? Notice sights, smells, and sounds. Then picture yourself handling this challenge with skill and strength. What does that feel like? Visualizing helps you rehearse for situations so you are ready when you encounter them in real life.

No-Calorie Treats and Rewards

19

Treat Yourself Right

Food is an essential part of life, and it tastes good. It is easily available (too available, some would say), often convenient, and relatively affordable for most of us. For many people, it is also a treat. Many of us have been conditioned since childhood to see food as a reward. However, if you are trying to lose weight, it may be helpful to break the pattern of using food as a reward or treat. To set yourself up for success, establish a list of no-calorie treats that you can use instead. Here are some ideas:

- Buy fresh flowers.
- Call a good friend on the telephone.
- Enjoy music.
- Take 10 minutes just to do nothing.
- Make a list of ten things for which you are truly grateful.
- Set aside a small amount of money each time you accomplish one of your goals. When you feel you need a treat or reward, use this money for that purpose. Perhaps you can have your nails done, buy a book, or get a massage.

What are some other ways you can reward yourself without food?

_____

_____

_____

_____

Refer to this list when you catch yourself looking for food as a reward.

Reward Your Successes

Although losing weight is a reward in and of itself, external rewards can be powerful incentives to stick to goals, such as following your calorie plan, keeping food records, and exercising. Think about incentives that would help motivate you. Perhaps you might enjoy setting aside time to read a good book or buying a shirt you want. Whatever the incentive is, it should be something that you give yourself if and only if you achieve the goal. Also, you need to resist the urge to decide afterward that you really don't deserve the reward after all and then not give it to yourself. If you have achieved your goal, you deserve the reward. That's the deal. Don't let yourself down.

One powerful incentive is money. You could motivate yourself by paying yourself a reward for meeting a goal or by paying a "fine" for not meeting it. In one study, one group of subjects agreed to write a check for 5 dollars to their favorite charity each week. If they lost weight that week, they got the check back. If they didn't lose weight, the check was cashed. Another group of subjects did not participate in the reward system. Week after week, the group that wrote the checks lost more weight than the group that did not. If you want to get serious about losing weight, consider setting up such an agreement. Ask a spouse, relative, or friend to help you stay honest and withhold or reimburse your checks.

Now that you've thought about ways to reward yourself without food, use the space below to record a goal you have set for yourself and how you will reward your success when you reach it.

My goal: _____

My reward: _____

Pasta or Prozac? Emotions and Eating

20

Think about a time when you have felt sad, angry, stressed, or discouraged. All you wanted was to feel better. The steps that will make you feel better, however, are not always obvious or easy to achieve. Resolving anger might require confronting someone. Resolving stress might require tough decisions, such as which tasks are priorities or which expectations need to change. Resolving feelings of sadness might require addressing some difficult issues.

One thing people rely on to make them feel better is eating. Eating can give a reliable and immediate feeling of relief. Food is easy. It's enjoyable. It's available. It's fast. In many ways, it's the perfect emotional escape. Some people describe food as the only reliable friend they have. Is it any wonder food is so hard to give up?

Remember this: Replacing the comfort of food with the comfort of something else is easier than replacing it with nothing. Removing food as your friend and therapist can leave you with an empty feeling. If this empty feeling is allowed to grow, as during a time of emotional distress, you are more likely to give in and eat something you shouldn't or to binge. The key is to recognize what role food serves in easing uncomfortable feelings and find an alternative.

Food and Emotions Exercise

Look at the following list of emotions. Which of them lead you to turn to food? Are there any other emotions that you would add to the list?

- Anger
- Boredom
- Sadness
- Happiness
- Fear
- Anxiety
- Loneliness
- Disappointment
- Guilt or shame
- Hurt

Record each emotion that leads you to food in the Food and Emotions chart below. Then use the space in the middle column to reflect on the reasons why you turn to food when you feel that way. (For example, for *anger* you might write, "When I am angry at my mother, I eat. I know she hates that I am overweight, so eating makes me feel like I'm getting back at her.")

Food and Emotions		
I turn to food when I feel...	I do this because ...	Instead of eating, I will ...
Stressed	Eating is a way to procrastinate and put off unpleasant tasks.	1. Get the least pleasant task out of the way first. 2. Break it down into smaller tasks that are easier to manage. 3. Reward myself with a 10-minute break after I finish.

Next, try to identify other, more effective ways to deal with those feelings. For example, John realized that when he was feeling stressed or overwhelmed by an unpleasant task, he ate as a way of procrastinating. (It's awfully hard to write a manuscript with a French fry in your hand.) He had to learn how to avoid procrastinating when faced with unpleasant tasks. Therefore, John decided he would do his least favorite task first to get it out of the way, break a task into smaller, manageable pieces, and give himself a no-calorie reward when he finished. These activities would directly deal with his procrastination.

They would reduce his stress and, therefore, keep him from eating as a form of relief.

Sometimes, you may be aware of a solution but feel overwhelmed by it. Break it into small steps and set progressive goals, just as you did for your weight loss goal. For example, suppose you decide to deal with feelings of loneliness by signing up for volunteer work. If this solution feels intimidating, you could write down the steps you must take. First, find out what agencies you'd be interested in helping out. Then find their telephone numbers. Next, call them. You can go from there.

You can use the third column of the Food and Emotions chart to write down some healthy ways you can deal with the emotions that normally lead you to turn to food. Other general ideas for dealing with feelings include keeping a journal, talking with people you trust, taking a walk, and listening to relaxing music.

Seeking Help

The best way to deal with a problem is to face it, not to hide from it by using food to cope with feelings. This direct approach can be threatening, but it is an important part of growing.

Some people may want to seek help from a counselor or psychologist when they reach this point. If you think you may need help, resources are available. You may ask someone you know who has been in counseling for suggestions. You can ask your physician for references. You also can call your community mental health agency. These agencies often provide services on a sliding scale of fees. Universities with graduate-level counseling programs also may provide counseling at reduced rates. Many insurance companies help pay for counseling services. You also might find help through self-help groups, such as Overeaters Anonymous. Although taking such a step can be frightening, it could be the first step in changing your life.

Hold That Thought 21

In some cases, the emotions you feel are the result of how you look at the world. We think up self-prescribed rules and interpretations that cloud our emotions. Renowned psychology and psychiatry experts Albert Ellis, Aaron Beck, and David Burns identified certain thought patterns that lead to frustration, depression, anger, and other unpleasant feelings that keep us from our weight loss goals. Some of these common "thought distortions" are listed in the following chart. Do any of them sound familiar to you?

Thought Distortions

Faulty View	What Is It?	What You Might Say	Constructive Reality Check
All-or-nothing thinking	You see the world as black and white. You're either on a plan or off it, with no room for imperfection.	"I already ate cookies. I've blown my chances to lose weight."	"I ate six cookies and went over my daily calorie budget by 300 calories. Next time I will limit myself to four cookies."
The fairness fallacy	You think you know what is fair, and you resent that life is unfair to you.	"Why should I have to watch what I eat? Others don't."	"Many people have to choose to be active and limit high-calorie foods to maintain a healthy weight."
Success blinders	You think that your successes don't count.	"I lost weight, but I didn't exercise enough, so I bet the loss was just water weight."	"Another week of weight loss! Next week I won't have as many obligations so I'll get more activity in."
Focusing on slip-ups	You give so much attention to problems, mistakes, or slip-ups that they are all you see.	"As usual, I caved in when we went to the Italian restaurant."	"I ate more pasta than I wanted, but I skipped the bread and wine, so I still improved."
"Awful-izing"	You make mountains out of molehills.	"Forget it! I've hurt my ankle. I'll never keep this weight off!"	"I hurt my ankle so I won't be walking for a few weeks. I will try weight training during that time."
Labeling	You assume the identity of a behavior or event that confirms a fear and decreases confidence.	"I'm a junk-food junkie," or "I'm a big failure."	"I like a lot of high-calorie foods, but I like carrots, chicken, and apples, too." Or "I slipped up, but I know I won't always follow my plan perfectly."
"Crystal balling"	You don't even give yourself a chance because you fear things won't turn out.	"I've never been able to lose weight before, so why should this time be different?"	"I have lined things up pretty well, and with support and self-confidence, I think I can do this."
Generalizing	You look at a single event or outcome and assume that will always be the case.	"See? That proves it. I didn't walk last week so I just won't stick with my plan."	"I will keep trying to revise my schedule."
"Shoulding"	You apply rules that demand certain behaviors you should be able to achieve.	"I should be able to walk past the doughnuts and not be tempted."	"I really love doughnuts, and when I see them I can't resist them. I'll avoid walking down that aisle."
Caustic comparisons	Your worth depends on how you compare to others rather than being based on your own standards.	"I go to the gym, but I am so much slower than everyone else. I feel inadequate."	"I just started working out, but I can already see some improvement in my fitness."
Abdicating power	You avoid responsibility by giving the power to change to someone or something else.	"I can't do this."	"I am the only one who can make these choices. It's challenging, but I have overcome other challenges in life'"
Blame game	You make others responsible for your actions.	"If she didn't cook with so much grease, I could cut my calories."	"I have explained my new eating goals, but I don't feel supported. I can start cooking my meals separately."

Source: For more information on thought distortions, see *Feeling Good: The New Mood Therapy* by David D. Burns (Harper Collins, 2000).

For a look at how these destructive thoughts can affect your weight, let's meet Mandy and Ann.

Mandy spends months building motivation to start her weight loss program. When she finally does start, she initially does great. She eats dry toast and baked fish, drinks gallons of water, and undertakes hours of physical activity. But after a couple of weeks of near-neurotic perfection, she starts to think about her favorite treat, white chocolate macadamia nut cookies. And she can't stop thinking about them. Not long after the thoughts of cookies start, Mandy bakes a batch, eats a few, and thoroughly enjoys them. Then, she feels guilt-ridden and she berates herself: "I can never stick with anything! I'm a failure!" As her morale slips lower, Mandy buries her exercise clothes in the closet beneath her "fat clothes." She quits tracking her food and eventually ends up 5 pounds heavier than when she started. For Mandy, this cycle of behavior fits a regular pattern.

For a time, Ann sticks to her eating and activity plan to the letter. Therefore, when some out-of-town guests stay with her for a few days, she figures, "I should be able to resist tempting treats while they're here." However, once they arrive, she feels so happy and thinks, "I'll just splurge a little. I'll get back on track after they leave." Three weeks later, Ann still isn't back on track. Even though she is exercising again, she is having had a hard time following her healthy eating plan. She tells herself that she is a failure for not being able to resist temptation and will never be able to lose weight. She is depressed and feels like a failure. Because she is depressed, she has been eating more. Because she has lost faith in herself, she is not trying as hard.

What are some of the ways you exhibit distorted thinking?

_____

_____

_____

By completing this exercise, you have taken the first step in changing a thought pattern—you have become aware of it. The next step is to challenge your thinking by replacing the distorted thoughts with a constructive reality check.

For example, once Mandy eats a single food item that she does not consider healthy and low calorie, she goes on a binge. She thinks that she has failed and lost control. She thinks to herself, "This day is a loss. You are so weak. You will never be able to stay on track. You may as well just write this day off and eat all the bad stuff you want."

If Mandy can learn to recognize these distorted thoughts, she can write down a rational response to counter them. For example, she could state that what she did was a normal human response to delicious food. She is not weak just because she ate some cookies. She could also calculate the actual number of calories she ate. She might find that the cookies she ate had 250. If possible, she could "deduct" the calories from another meal or snack that day. If not, she could simply realize that she ate 250 calories more than she wanted to that day, and realize that 250 calories is not enough to make or break a weight loss program.

Ann thinks she was stupid to splurge when her guests visited. Maybe she didn't realize how hard it would be to get back to her plan, but that does not mean she is a failure. Ann could challenge her thoughts by recognizing and accepting that she will never have perfect eating and exercise habits all the time. Just because she has had a rough few weeks does not mean that she will not succeed. It just means she has had a rough few weeks.

There will always be events that will interfere with your goals. The trick is to minimize the number of such events. On Thanksgiving, for example, many people find it difficult to stick with their weight loss plans. Thanksgiving is only one day out of 365. Instead of letting your actions on one bad day derail your plans, recognize that what you do on the other 364 days is far more important.

To learn new ways of thinking, take 10 minutes each day to reflect and look at the things you are saying to yourself. Are they valid thoughts, or are you engaging in distorted thinking? Make it a practice to replace these messages with productive, nonjudgmental messages. Take a moment now to write down some rational thoughts that refute your distorted thinking.

_____

_____

_____

Although changing the way you think is very difficult, it is also very important. Become aware of the decisions you make. If you are tempted by food in a vending machine, pause for a moment. Recognize that you are making a decision either in favor of or against your weight management plan. The decision to eat the food is a valid one, even if that choice pushes you over your calorie limit that day. You will inevitably make such choices at times. But when you do make those choices, it is important that you accept them and move on. To stew about a decision and turn it into a statement "proving" your inherent inability to lose weight is not valid. Further, it is not helpful to feel that because you were not perfect, you have the green light to eat any and all high-calorie foods.

22 'Tis the Season: Special Situations

Vacations and holidays are times to let down your guard, relax, and have fun. They are also times when people tend to stray from their weight loss plans. This chapter offers some tips to help you stay on track.

One key to success is establishing a game plan. Carlos went on a Caribbean cruise while trying to lose weight and improve his health. Cruises are well known for having delicious, high-calorie foods available in abundance at all hours of the day and night. Such a spread would be hard to resist. But Carlos made plans in advance of his trip. He telephoned the travel agent and let her know that he had certain dietary needs, which the chef of the ship willingly accommodated. When he returned from the cruise, Carlos reported having had a great time, and he did not gain any weight—a remarkable feat for anyone!

You can also develop strategies to reduce temptation during the holidays. If you go to a potluck dinner, for example, bring a low-calorie dish so that you'll have at least one healthy choice. When neighbors and friends bring you cookies, try one or two of your favorite kinds, and then get the remaining cookies out of the house (even if you have to throw them out or give them away).

At holiday meals, fill most of your plate with the low-calorie foods, leaving room for only one bite of each of the other foods. Tell your companions that you intend to have only one plate of food. If you do this, you may be too embarrassed to get seconds.

Before you attend a high-calorie affair or go on vacation, remember all the strategies you have learned from this workbook:

- Set a goal and think about how you will achieve it. (For example, what specific steps can you plan to make activities, not food, the center of the party or vacation?) Write your goal down and keep it with you as a reminder.
- Visualize yourself successfully engaging in the behaviors you want to practice.
- Remember that holidays and vacations are special times that are meant to be enjoyed, but that there is no excuse for overindulging.

Write down some specific strategies you can use during special occasions to stick to your weight loss plan.

On vacation, I will:

1. _____

2. _____

3. _____

4. _____

5. _____

During holidays and parties, I will:

1. _____

2. _____

3. _____

4. _____

5. _____

23 First Things First: Setting Priorities

So much to do, so little time! With so many competing demands, it's easy to let your weight loss commitment fall into the background. There will be days when exercising just doesn't seem to fit in your schedule or when it feels like too much of a bother to weigh and measure portion sizes or plan a week's worth of meals in advance. Sometimes, if you're a parent, you just won't want to fight with your kids when they ask you to buy them the snack cakes they love. Sometimes, you will feel like you don't have the emotional energy to continue to ask your family for support, or to send a wrong order back to the kitchen at a restaurant.

But you must stay committed! These little, everyday decisions add up to weight loss success. Yes, losing weight takes work. No, it never lets up. Many things are tugging at you, trying to grab your attention. But healthy eating and physical activity must receive priority.

To make weight loss a priority, you may have to say "no" even when it's hard to do so. You may have to tell your family you can't have sweets in the house for a while, even if they beg or complain. Stand your ground. Remind them that their support is important to you.

Making weight loss a priority also means no more excuses. Resist the belief that there is no good day for exercise, nothing to eat but a candy bar, no time to keep your food records, and no easy way to become assertive about making sure your needs are met. At times, your commitments will be difficult to keep, but these commitments propel you onward, through the fog, to your weight and health goals.

Are there people, events, or circumstances that interfere with your weight loss priorities? List them here:

_____

_____

_____

_____

Now write down some ways in which you can make your weight loss the priority despite these factors:

_____

_____

_____

_____

In It for the Long Haul: Weight Maintenance

24

While you are in the weight loss stage, there is a beginning and an end—a finish line (reaching your goal weight). During the weight maintenance stage, however, there is no end. Maintaining weight loss over the long term is a lifelong process, and it can be at least as difficult as the process of losing weight.

The Challenges of Weight Maintenance

While you are losing weight, you are rewarded along the way by things like watching the number on the scale drop, buying new clothes in smaller sizes, and attracting compliments. During weight maintenance, however, you are working almost as hard just to stay the same. The smaller clothes are no longer new. The compliments come less frequently. Perhaps some of the dreams that you thought would be realized when you lost weight have not been fulfilled.

At times, you may ask yourself why you carry on. Is staying at your goal weight really worth the effort? This sort of question is common, because we tend to forget pain as we move away from it. Time heals wounds, including the wounds associated with being overweight.

If you are struggling with the maintenance stage, these reflective activities may help inspire you to stay on track:

- **Reflect on the reasons why you wanted to lose weight.** (You may wish to look back at Chapter 1.) Perhaps you'll remember painful moments, such as how it felt when you could not find a chair to sit in, when the neighbor's child made fun of you, or when your doctor told you that you would have to take insulin if you didn't lose weight.

- **List some of the advantages you have gained by losing weight.** Perhaps you can play with your kids for longer periods because your stamina has improved. Maybe you feel proud of your accomplishment. Perhaps your knee pain has abated. Have you started taking these things for granted?

_____

_____

_____

- **Explore why maintaining your weight loss is so difficult at times.** Have you forgotten the skills you learned while you were losing weight? Has it become difficult to accept the reality that you must continue to devote so much time to physical activity? Is your calorie budget at a level you really don't want to maintain?

_____

_____

_____

Perhaps you can find other paths to the same goal. For example, maybe you can change how you divide up your calorie budget so that you can occasionally have some of your favorite foods. Maybe you'll decide to change your daily physical activity plan from a 45-minute session to three bouts of 15 minutes. Record your ideas below.

_____

_____

_____

In the process of learning how to maintain your new, lower body weight, you may gain back a few pounds. That may be okay. You will probably not follow all the healthy eating principles perfectly. Remember that you are learning new skills and that you will stumble at times. The important thing is that you continue to practice and to learn and grow when you do stumble.

How to Know If You're Backsliding

Because weight changes are the result of multiple food and activity choices made over time, it's not always clear when you are slipping. Here are some strategies you can use to evaluate your situation:

- **Have a "red-flag" weight or pant size.** Weight is the most objective measure of how you're doing (although it's important to recognize that your weight will always fluctuate a bit from day to day). After you have reached your goal weight and are working to stay close to it, ask yourself: "What is the weight (or pant size) that will tell me I'm off track and need to get back on plan?"

Red-flag weight: _____ or Red-flag pant size: _____

- **Analyze your behavior patterns.** Look for slip-ups in your day-to-day food and activity patterns. Have you started relapsing on the key behaviors that have contributed to your success? For example, have you started skipping your lunchtime walks? Have you put the candy jar on your desk again? Have you started buying lunch again instead of bringing one from home? Have you reinstated visits to the Cookie Connection? List some behaviors that will serve as "relapse warnings."

_____

_____

_____

_____

- **Be aware of your decisions.** Each day we make many decisions regarding our weight, whether we are aware of them or not. We choose what to eat at meals, whether we will take the stairs or the elevator, whether to visit the vending machine, whether to stop by the dozens of restaurants we pass, whether we will buy a candy bar when we fill the car with gas. There are many opportunities to stray from your eating and activity plans. The flip side is there are also many opportunities in a day to make decisions in favor of weight management. Every time you pass a vending machine or restaurant without stopping, you have succeeded. We don't often see this part of the weight management picture. Because weight management is a lifelong process, you can expect that you will make both decisions that support weight management and decisions that do not. You achieve a favorable outcome, though, when you make more good decisions than bad ones. The balance will show on the scale.

Maintenance, the last—and longest—stage of the weight loss journey, is conceivably the most important. Never think that the road will be without potholes. It has been said that there are some things people can learn only through tribulation, or that the only way out of a problem is to work through it. Too often in life, people want to change, but they give up on their goals when things get tough. They may trick themselves into thinking that they should postpone things—that somehow, it will be easier next time. So, they hit the wall, turn back, hit the wall again, and turn back again. However, it is only by persisting and gradually breaking through the wall that the dream of lifelong weight loss becomes a reality. Keep chipping at the wall, one choice at a time, until *your* dream becomes a reality!

Eating Self-Assessment

Taking the Self-Assessment

Instructions: For each question, circle the answer that best describes you. Then count how many responses you have from each column and write this number in the TOTAL row for that chart. When you have completed the charts for Parts A through F, use the Summary Chart to collect your totals for the entire assessment.

Part A: Food Choices

	Option 1	Option 2	Option 3
I eat fried foods:	More than 3 times a week	1–3 times a week	Less than once a week
I consume these dairy products:	Whole milk or regular cheese	Low-fat milk and reduced fat cheese	Fat-free (skim) milk and nonfat cheese
I drink alcohol (1 drink = 12 ounces beer, 1½ ounces hard liquor, or 5 ounces wine):	More than 2 drinks a day	1–2 drinks per day or less	0 drinks per day
I often eat sweets, like candies, cakes, cookies, and pies:	I easily eat the equivalent of ½ pack of cookies or ½ gallon of ice cream in a day.	More than 4 small cookies or equivalent a day	Less than 1–2 small cookies a day; I prefer fruit
I eat fatty foods such as bacon, sausage, and the skin of chicken:	At least once a day	3–5 times a week	Less than 3 times a week
I drink regular sodas or sugar-sweetened drinks (1 serving = 12-ounce can):	More than one a day	3–5 servings per week	Less than 3 servings a week
At a party, I would have a plate with:	Mini quiches, cheese, and chips	Swedish meatballs and crackers	Vegetables
TOTAL			

Part B: Portion Sizes

	Option 1	Option 2	Option 3
If the restaurant offers free refills (sodas, chips, bread, and so on), I get refills:	Often	Sometimes	Never
I usually get large or extra-large servings:	Often	Sometimes	Never
I think a serving of steak is:	16 ounces	8 ounces	3 ounces
My idea of dessert is:	A half gallon of ice cream	A big bowl of ice cream	A tennis ball–sized scoop of ice cream
My serving of meat is usually the size of:	A steno pad	Two decks of cards	A deck of cards
I start my first serving already thinking of seconds and thirds:	Often	Sometimes	Never
If someone brings doughnuts to work, I usually have:	More than 2	1–2 doughnuts	Less than 1 doughnut
TOTAL			

Part C: Eating Patterns

	Option 1	Option 2	Option 3
I skip breakfast:	Often	Sometimes	Never
I eat less than 3 times a day:	Often	Sometimes	Never
I make it a point to clean my plate:	Often	Sometimes	Never
I am usually the first to finish my meal:	Often	Sometimes	Never
I get very hungry and then eat until I am overfull:	Often	Sometimes	Never
I get so hungry I end up grabbing the first available thing I find:	Often	Sometimes	Never
Even if I am not hungry, I eat when it's mealtime:	Often	Sometimes	Never
TOTAL			

Part D: Awareness of Hunger

	Option 1	Option 2	Option 3
I eat while doing other things and find I have eaten more than I intended:	Often	Sometimes	Never
I clean my plate without thinking:	Often	Sometimes	Never
I can't tell when I am hungry:	Often	Sometimes	Never
I often find that I have eaten more than I intended just because food was there:	Often	Sometimes	Never
I never get hungry because I eat all the time:	Often	Sometimes	Never
I feel uncomfortably full after eating:	Often	Sometimes	Never
I eat for any reason but hunger:	Often	Sometimes	Never
TOTAL			

Part E: Emotional and Social Eating

	Option 1	Option 2	Option 3
I eat more when I am alone or I eat more when I am with others:	Often	Sometimes	Never
I wake up thinking about food and think about it most of the time:	Often	Sometimes	Never
I eat to deal with my feelings (stress, sadness, boredom, and so on):	Often	Sometimes	Never
I am the one to bring the food to work or parties. People look to me for that:	Often	Sometimes	Never
I eat for something to do:	Often	Sometimes	Never
I eat "at people" when they comment on my weight:	Often	Sometimes	Never
I don't have a care in the world when I'm eating:	Often	Sometimes	Never
TOTAL			

Part F: Environmental Cues

	Option 1	Option 2	Option 3
If I see food sitting out, I am tempted to eat it:	Often	Sometimes	Never
Food ads send me straight to the kitchen:	Often	Sometimes	Never
I can't pass a bakery without getting a pastry:	Often	Sometimes	Never
I get distracted by the food table at parties:	Often	Sometimes	Never
I salivate when I drive past my favorite restaurants:	Often	Sometimes	Never
The more I'm served, the more I eat:	Often	Sometimes	Never
I snack without realizing it:	Often	Sometimes	Never
TOTAL			

Summary Chart

	Totals for Option 1	Totals for Option 2	Totals for Option 3
Part A: Food choices			
Part B: Portion sizes			
Part C: Eating patterns			
Part D: Awareness of hunger			
Part E: Emotional and social eating			
Part F: Environmental cues			

Understanding Your Patterns and Setting Goals

Review the Summary Chart and notice the parts where you have many Option 1 answers. These indicate a big area for improvement. Checks in the middle column (Option 2) indicate a possible area for improvement. Read on for possible goals for your biggest problem areas, and write down goals for yourself.

Part A: Food Choices

If you chose Option 1 most of the time in Part A: Food Choices, this indicates that part of your weight problem is due to eating high-calorie foods or drinks.

Possible goals:

- Keep a food journal, including calorie counts (you may also want to track amounts of fat, sugar, and protein).
- Start reading calorie information on food labels and restaurant menus (ask the server if you can't find calorie information), and looking up the number of calories in food.
- Use low-calorie condiments, such as mustard, fat-free dressing, sugar-free jelly, and salsa, instead of butter, jam, cream cheese, mayonnaise, and other high-fat condiments.

- At meals, fill half of your plate with fruits and vegetables and the other half with meat or another lean protein food and a healthy starch or whole grain, such as brown rice.
- Eliminate calorie-containing drinks, including alcohol. Calories from liquids can add up fast. One small soft drink (20 ounces) has 240 calories. A large soft drink can have over 500 calories—enough to gain 1 pound a week if you drink one a day. A medium-sized white chocolate mocha has about 500 calories. Be sure to also check the labels of specialty waters for the calories and grams of sugar. Some contain high amounts of sugar.
- Limit high-sugar foods (cookies, jellies, cakes, candy, ice cream, and so on).

Part B: Portion Sizes

If you chose Option 1 most of the time in Part B: Portion Sizes, this indicates that part of your weight problem is due to eating large amounts of food. Focusing on portion sizes will help.

Possible goals:

- Keep a food journal, including records of portion sizes and the calories in those portions.
- Weigh and measure your portions. Compare the calories in your portions to the calories in standard portion sizes.
- Use smaller plates, cups, and bowls.
- Chew each bite 20 times or set a timer to help you eat more slowly.
- Order small or medium servings instead of large ones. If you're still hungry, add a vegetable or fruit.
- Avoid buffets and "all you can eat" restaurants.
- Avoid going back for second helpings.
- Get small portions of foods, including small-sized prepackaged portions.

Part C: Eating Patterns

If you chose Option 1 most of the time in Part C: Eating Patterns, this indicates that part of your weight problem is due to skipping meals, which may make you vulnerable to poor food choices or overeating.

Possible goals:

- Keep a food journal, including records of meal and snack times and your hunger levels. Look for patterns.
- Eat breakfast (a protein drink or a protein bar is a quick option).
- Eat three nutritious meals a day and include a lean protein food, fruits and/or vegetables, and whole grains at each meal. Don't wait until you are famished to eat.
- Keep healthy snacks available in case you get hungry between meals.
- Buy quick, low-calorie frozen meals for the week. Make sure they include a lean protein food and a vegetable.
- Set an alarm on your cell phone or computer to remind you to eat.
- Develop a menu plan that will work with your lifestyle.

Part D: Awareness of Hunger

If you chose Option 1 most of the time in Part D: Awareness of Hunger, this indicates that part of your weight problem is due to not being able to notice or identify physical sensations of hunger for food.

Possible goals:

- Keep a food journal, including records of meal and snack times and your hunger levels.
- Before you eat, close your eyes and think about why you are eating. Notice the feeling in your body. Notice how you feel after each bite. Take time to eat, and stop eating when you start to feel satisfied (or no longer feel hungry), even if your plate is not empty.
- Set a timer while you eat to slow you down. Notice your hunger level before you eat.
- When you are indulging in a calorie-rich food, slowly savor each bite. You may find that you are satisfied before you even finish.

Part E: Emotional and Social Eating

If you chose Option 1 most of the time in Part E: Emotional and Social Eating, this indicates that part of your weight problem is due to using food as a coping strategy or to deal with social situations.

Possible goals:

- Keep a food journal, including records of foods eaten and your emotional state before and after eating. Also, track how any thoughts and events trigger your emotions.
- Take an assertiveness training class.
- Keep a journal of your experiences, thoughts, and feelings.
- Learn and practice relaxation techniques, including how to prioritize and break down tasks.
- Have a list of friends you can call and talk with about whatever is going on.
- Consider joining a program that deals with emotional eating, such as Overeaters Anonymous.
- Take a walk to raise your "feel good" brain chemistry.
- Seek counseling.
- Make a list of activities other than eating that help you cope with emotions.

Part F: Environmental Cues

If you chose Option 1 most of the time in Part F: Environmental Cues, this indicates that part of your weight problem is due to sensitivity to sights and smells of food.

Possible goals:

- Keep a food journal, including notes about events that trigger eating.
- Take alternative routes to places you routinely go, so you do not see the restaurants that usually tempt you on your way.
- Leave the room or turn the volume down during commercials.
- Ask family, friends, and coworkers not to bring you unhealthy snacks or treats.

Source: Appendix A is adapted with permission from Piechota, Toni. The Complete Counseling Kit for Weight Loss Surgery. Chicago, IL: Academy of Nutrition and Dietetics; 2012.

Digital Resources

Apps and Websites

SuperTracker (www.supertracker.usda.gov)

The U.S. Department of Agriculture's free online program helps you create a personalized nutrition and physical activity plan to help you lose weight. The site offers a food and physical activity tracker to help you track your progress and meet your goals.

MyFitnessPal (www.myfitnesspal.com)

This free website and mobile app is an easy-to-use food and physical activity tracker with an extensive database of foods, including many restaurant items. It will help you set a daily calorie target based on your personal nutritional needs and activity level. It syncs up with wearable activity trackers, such as FitBit. The message boards offer a place to find support from other members.

MapMyFitness (www.mapmyfitness.com)

With this website and app, you choose your activity—walking, jogging, biking, or any number of others in the database. When you start your workout, your phone's built-in GPS tracks your route, speed, distance, duration, and pace as well as the number calories you burn. You can save routes, share on social media, set goals, and track nutrition, too.

Noom Coach (for iPhone) and Noom Weight (for Android) (www.noom.com)

In addition to letting you track food and activities, Noom's app provides daily coaching to help you reach your goals. It has an integrated pedometer so your phone can be used to track your steps.

Fitocracy (www.fitocracy.com)

Making activity fun, this app uses elements of video gaming, such as power-ups and challenges, to reward you for tracking workouts. A social component allows you to compete against friends or other users.

The 7-Minute Scientific Workout (www.7-min.com)

The free website and app alternates 30 seconds of high-energy exercises, such as jumping jacks, push-ups, squats, and planks, with 10 seconds of rest.

Eat Slower

As the name implies, this app helps you practice mindful eating through a timer that vibrates when it's time to take the next bite. Available for Apple and Android phones.

HealthyWage (www.healthywage.com)

Add a financial incentive to your weight loss effort by signing up for a money-based challenge that helps you commit to a start date and see your goals through to the end. Place a bet that you'll reach your goal. If you don't, you lose your money. If you do, you win money.

Wearable Activity Trackers

FitBit, Omron, and Jawbone are just a few of the brands of wearable technology that have recently emerged in the marketplace. Usually worn on your wrist or clipped onto your clothing, these gadgets can track things like movement, heart rate, sleep, and calories. The data sync to an accompanying website or app.

Sample Goal Record Sheet

Use a chart like this one to help you stay on track with your eating and activity goals. Write down your goals, and place a checkmark in the boxes for each day you achieve them.

Goals	Sun	Mon	Tue	Wed	Thu	Fri	Sat
Walk 30 minutes		✔	✔	✔	✔	✔	
Eat 5 servings of fruits and vegetables	✔	✔			✔		
Keep within my calorie budget	✔	✔	✔	✔	✔		